The Silent Sound

The Silent Sound

Thoughts and theories
for a new century

John Evans

Ross-Evans

British Library Cataloguing in Publication Data

Evans, John
The silent sound: thoughts and theories for a new century
1. Science - Philosophy
I. Title
501

ISBN   1 874498 04 0

Printed by
The Burlington Press
1 Station Road, Foxton,
Cambridge CB2 6SW

Published by
Ross-Evans
St. Mary's House, 47 High Street, Trumpington,
Cambridge CB2 2HZ

To

Jewel, Cathy, Melanie, Alison, and John

Preface

This book is essentially for my friends, and I make no apology for the personal and direct style of writing. It is a sequel to the book *Mind, Body and Electromagnetism* first published in 1985. It is less technical with almost no mathematical content; and even if the first four chapters are still too specialised for some, I hope the later chapters provide thoughts and ideas of general interest.

In so far as one can categorise the book, there are three fairly distinct yet related lines of thought. The first deals with new thinking in the life sciences, with special emphasis on basic problems of growth and form. With all the recent attention given to the Human Genome Project, few seem to realise that we have almost no understanding about the construction of a cell, or groups of cells, or organs, or the overall structure. The subject of *Bioelectromagnetism* is gradually gaining ground, with new concepts about the control of growth processes, and new applications in medicine.

The second concerns social problems, and how we might move on to a more co-operative society. Darwinism, applied to social issues, makes a nonsense of all our attempts to develop a civilised democratic society. It also contradicts the basic tenets of any legal system which assumes the existence of individual freewill and responsibility.

The third contains personal views and thoughts that do not get an airing in the current academic climate. For those who try to widen the scope into certain medical and psychological areas that challenge reductionist beliefs, there is little chance of acceptance or advancement. Some professional colleagues may even interpret such criticisms as *anti-science;* but my opinion is that, by rejecting all views outside current scientific assumptions, it is they who help to undermine the status of science in our society.

As with the previous book, each chapter is relatively self-contained, and the reader should find little difficulty taking things out of order. However, in the more difficult matters of biophysics, there is some overlapping of material to help make individual chapters reasonably independent and intelligible. Those who want to follow up some of the electromagnetic ideas can do so through the ROSS computer language (ross-evans.co.uk).

John Evans
Cambridge
August 2001

Acknowledgements

To friends past and present - William Bush, Ivan Cane, Dave Deamer, Michael Franklin, Eileen Ison, Iorwerth John, Cyril Jones, Tidu Maini, Lindesay Moffatt, Douglas Ross, Leslie Smith, Robin Springham, Betty Shepherd, Jean Stubbs, Peter Ward, Doug Webb, and the whole Cottee family - I am so grateful for the kindnesses, companionship, letters, music, and conversation. I hope that, despite absent years, you will find something recognisable in the style and content. To those who have commented freely and frankly on the text - Michele Bailey, Alan Burgess, Jean Byrom, Peter Cottee, Larissa Fradkin, Ivor Gillbe, Thomas Harder, Lin Hardiman, Jill Maguire, Tamlin Simpson-Nicholl, Blandine Walker - I am greatly indebted. Many thanks to Louise Hall and Chris Mortimer for the computer layout. And finally a special word of appreciation to Viktor Slaninka who obtained two invaluable volumes directly from the Nikola Tesla Museum in Belgrade during the recent troubled times.

Contents

Chapter One

New Directions in Science

The beginning of the twentieth century was an exciting time in many aspects of science. In the life sciences, Mendel's work on the mechanisms of inheritance was rediscovered, and this rescued Darwin's major thesis. Prior to this, Darwinian concepts were losing their appeal, mathematicians having decided that the blending of genetic material could only lead to uniformity, not diversity. In physics, there were the first papers in Relativity and Quantum Mechanics, these representing the beginnings of a move away from the strict determinism of nineteenth-century field and electromagnetic theory. In technology, Nikola Tesla was experimenting with ionospheric resonance and power transmission without wires.

To many scientific writers, the new theoretical developments ushered in a different world view, one that would not only overturn an old science, but also refashion our attitudes towards religious and traditional beliefs. In my opinion, this was overstated. In the physical sciences, the actual practice of research continued along much the same lines, and the vast majority of scientists never got near to using the Einstein concepts of space-time. Our space technology depended on Newtonian mechanics, and almost all our radio technology was developed from the work of Faraday and Maxwell and other nineteenth century figures. Tesla, who single-handedly pioneered so many of the basic developments in alternating current, relied entirely on classical theory.

After the first models of the atom that came from classical ideas, quantum mechanics developed along separate lines, exploring the nature of matter at the atomic and subatomic levels, and the associated high-

1

frequency radiations. It developed probabilistic theories that were independent of both classical electromagnetics and relativity. By contrast, the *Special Theory of Relativity* is often thought of as putting the finishing touches to the electromagnetic equations of Clerk Maxwell and his contemporaries.

In the last three decades, there have been some major new developments in physics through exploring the nature of space and time at levels very far below the atomic level - in fact involving distances and times at the ultimate limits of space-time and of the order of 10^{-33} cms. In the new *String* theorising, the various point-particles of the subatomic world are replaced by vibrating strings or membranes of finite but minimal size, and of different frequencies. Space-time itself, what used to be called the *ether*, has a granular structure with elements of minimum dimensions. In these terms, *field* is again the basic entity, and the nineteenth-century equations remain fundamental. Between the atomic scale and the string dimensions billions of times smaller, we are now conscious of a vast unexplored desert.

For those of us studying the extremely low frequencies (ELF) of biological systems, the new physics is entirely encouraging, giving renewed emphasis to classical concepts, and tending to free us from the strange criticisms of high-frequency specialists. For instance, we used to be told that, because very low electromagnetic frequencies have huge wavelengths, it required a massive aerial to detect them. Anyone with the simplest knowledge of radio knows that we can build tiny circuits that can respond to extremely high or low frequencies, this depending on the electromagnetic properties (capacitance, resistance, inductance) of the components used. Similarly the cell structures of all organic life have the necessary electromagnetic properties that generate and respond to very low vibrations.

Biologists now understand the electrical conduction of individual nerve cells in terms of electrical gradients across the outer membrane containing special protein gates for potassium and sodium ions. Membranes of nerve and muscle cells sustain a resting potential of about -70 millivolts, and which, across a thickness of two molecules, is

2

equivalent to a field of millions of volts per metre. Clearly, the membranes are always in a highly energised state. The nerve pulse produces a change to about +30 mV, and this allows sodium ions to drift inwards, and potassium ions outwards.

The nerve cell is like a tree, with one major trunk or *axon* emanating from the cell body, together with many smaller roots or *dendrites*. Within much of the nervous system, information is received through the dendrites, and then communicated on through the axon to other cells. Within the brain, it seems that both input and output are largely controlled through the dendrites; and by such means, one nerve cell may be in communication with as many as 10,000 other cells. Given the trillions of nerve cells, the degree of intercommunication is of an incredible order.

In modern studies, we are beginning to investigate the properties of bundles of nerve fibres in simpler engineering terms. Groups of nerve pulses, which communicate information to other nerve and muscle cells, flow along axons at a speed of the order of a few metres a second - only a fraction of the conduction speed of electrons in a normal conductor which travel close to the speed of light. As the frequencies in the body are of the order of about 100 cycles a second - in the audio range and below - this gives a wavelength or scale of the order of centimetres. The actual frequency range of electrical signals corresponds quite closely with our voice range - the mechanical and electrical being intimately interconnected in the body.

Other cells have an electrical field across the membrane of about -30 mV, and all are subject to the intrinsic fields of the cellular environment. As moving pulses and charges are inevitably accompanied by both electric and magnetic fields, there is an electromagnetic field pervading every organ, and the whole system. With suitable screening out of the earth's field, this human magnetic field was carefully measured by David Cohen in the 1970s around the heart and the head. The frequencies naturally corresponded with the major nerve frequencies, and the intensity just outside the body was about a millionth of the earth's field.

Classical electromagnetics, not quantum theory, provides an excellent framework for studying ELF fields, and for indicating sensible experiments to carry out. Even as far back as the 1840s, there were experiments in audio-frequency fields (sometimes called "magnetic music"), including the interesting observation that bent metal objects would tend to straighten in such a field. Later on, it was appreciated that all electromagnetic fields have a mechanical effect such as we get with the mains hum of a transformer, or the force that turns an electric motor. There is a simple rationale in classical theory in that an electric field E, in conjunction with a magnetic field H, will always produce a mechanical force proportional to E x H.

One hesitates to say this, but quantum physicists do sometimes give the impression that they have largely forgotten some of this elementary knowledge - and younger ones possibly never learnt it. In fact, for much of the twentieth century, they tried to eliminate the notion of field altogether, replacing it by particles moving in empty space. There was certainly a period during the 1970s and 1980s when one sensed a definitive reluctance to talk about electric and magnetic fields in some of the scientific journals. This in turn allowed scientists of electricity companies to make curious statements to the effect that there was no scientific rationale for power lines of 50 or 60 Hz (cycles per second) having any effect on human beings. These fields, passing through the body, induce ionic currents that can adversely affect the natural rhythms of the nervous system vibrating at a similar rate.

Through national epidemiological studies in several countries, there is now considerable evidence that continuous exposure to mains fields at about three times normal background levels has long-term effects, particularly leukemia in children. Many of us know of individual cases which, at the personal level, tend to be more convincing than large statistical studies. We are all exposed to these fields to some extent in our houses and offices, and there seems to be a threshold of about three milligauss which has cancer-inducing properties.

Probably the most important study of childhood leukemia, and certainly the most quoted, was that done by Nancy Wertheimer in Denver in the 1970s, and published in the *American Journal of Epidemiology* in

1979. She began with no thoughts of an electromagnetic cause; but in constantly seeing a black cylindrical transformer on a pole near the houses in question, she brought in a physicist friend to help. They found significant fields of a few milliguass near the transformers, and near the supply leads into the houses. Similar studies in Sweden, Russia, and Canada have supported the Denver conclusions; and just recently, there has at long last been some confirmation in Britain.

In the USA, Ross Adey and Robert Becker have been the major pioneers in discovering specific ELF effects, and rationalising the leukemia findings. Becker's work focused on the electrical processes involved in the regeneration of tissues and organs. Ross Adey experimented with very specific low frequencies below 100 Hz on the brains of chickens and cats, and related the fields to interference with the natural calcium-ion processes of the nervous system. In particular, he suggested that the large protein molecules in the cell membrane, that control movement in and out of the cell, were affected.

In Russia, Alexander Dubrov brought together hundreds of papers relating to the role of the earth's geomagnetic field (GMF) in organic processes. His famous book, *The Geomagnetic Field and Life*, essentially proposed a new evolutionary theory, one not based on chance and probability, but through the causal mechanisms of the electromagnetic environment. All aspects of the field were taken into account: the horizontal and vertical components, the angle between them (*dip*), the low-frequency oscillations between the ionosphere and the earth, the daily *circadian* rhythms caused by the earth's rotation, and the complete reversal of north and south poles about every half-million years. In his opinion, molecules and genes are polarised into left and right forms at the beginning of life through the GMF; and the continuous biochemical changes in our body and emotional moods reflect the natural rhythms around us. Major species changes take place during the field reversals.

Definitive work has been done at the Ramón y Cahal hospital in Madrid, subjecting chicken embryos to various frequencies and intensities. In a spectacular series of experiments in 1980, José Delgado and Jocelyne Leal found that, at 100 Hz and 12 milligauss, all the embryos were damaged. At higher and lower frequencies and intensities - they tried nine different combinations - the effects were less noticeable. Somehow, the field was interfering with the normal growth processes.

That is one side of the coin. On the other side, we now have considerable evidence about the positive use of audio frequencies, using either current input or electromagnetic fields. The most successful applications have involved the repair of bones, wound healing, and pain control in childbirth. Breast cancer has been successfully treated in Sweden with pulsed currents by Dr Nordenström at the Karolinska Institute. There is some evidence of a reversal of other cancers with specific frequencies. Unfortunately, knowledge of fields and frequencies is very sparse, mainly because life scientists have discouraged any ideas suggestive of *vitalism* for most of the twentieth century.

My own efforts have been a mixture of computer analysis and simple oscillator experiments. Using software simulations, I have endeavoured to understand how certain patterns of audio-frequency waveforms could create the geometry of our own bodies, from the cellular to the overall structure. In addition, I have experimented for many years with audio-frequency oscillators that apply small currents to the skin and nerves, and low intensity electromagnetic fields to the body generally.

With oscillators, my initial experimentation centred on acupuncture concepts, and quickly confirmed the reality of the acupoints. In fact, it did rather more: it removed any mystery about them. Between two general points on the skin, the resistance to audio-frequency currents is of the order of a million ohms. Between two acupoints, or between two areas of exposed muscle, the resistance goes down dramatically to something of the order of a few hundred ohms. This would suggest that the acupoints are simply those positions on the skin where the muscle cells are extremely close to the skin surface.

From this, I went on to try to assess the effects of specific octaves, and specific frequencies. At a few volts and a few milliamps, lower octaves can give a strong tingling effect. Above 1,000 Hz, there is hardly any effect at all - for the simple reason that nerves cells cannot respond at this rate because of the time delays between nerve and muscle junctions. Specific frequencies around the note C seemed generally beneficial; those around F or G tended to bring on cold symptoms to which I have always been very prone.

My recent experimentation has been almost exclusively on whole-body procedures - from the feet to the ears or hands. As this must involve the whole spinal system, it may be a sensible way to strengthen electrical activity in the body. I discovered by accident one day a path - presumably the spinal cord itself - of almost no resistance from the pelvis to the neck, and this had the effect of a major shock from a power line. However, the feet-hands path is completely safe at 10-20 volts, and there is an interesting decrease in resistance every time one breathes in. After about two minutes, the resistance is often about one quarter of the initial resistance. This I understand is consistent with neurological findings in that continuous electrical pressure on the nerves increases conductivity - lowers resistance.

Many are now postulating the existence of new types of *fields* to account for the great complexities of organic phenomena. Some of this stems from military sources, who have as much knowledge of low-frequency phenomena as anyone, and have in fact financed much of the research. Their current experiments in Alaska shown recently on television, and that artificially generate ELF waves from the ionosphere, indicate sophisticated understanding of low-frequency electromagnetic phenomena. Nikola Tesla is the only person to have done similar experiments. With relatively simple equipment, he produced potentials of hundred million volts in the Colorado Desert in 1899, and generated stationary waves involving the whole earth and the upper atmosphere. His findings, retained in the Tesla Museum in Belgrade, and discussed in Chapter 3, are now being seriously studied.

I have no wish to discourage new theorising about informational fields, subtle fields, scalar fields, a fifth force, zero-point energy, cancelling fields, biogravitational energy, and other speculations. But for me, there is so much straightforward research to be done with electromagnetic fields which our major scientific institutions can support without theoretical reservations. Furthermore, if the new string theorising, with electromagnetic field concepts as central, are on the right lines, then electromagnetic theory will lead us on naturally to explore quite new subtleties.

During the last two decades, we have begun to demonstrate and understand how the electric and magnetic fields and waves affect fundamental processes of organic life on this planet, from the inter-cellular signalling of our own internal vibrations, to ionospheric waves that resonate with our brain rhythms. This is beginning to help in the exploration of basic growth and healing processes, and allows us to envisage quite new forms of medicine based on rational electromagnetic principles. In some aspects, we will be resuming the research of the 1890s. However, we return with a new electro-chemical knowledge of nerves and muscles and cells, and new electronic technologies.

The development of computers has brought not only many improvements in instrumentation, but also new concepts and a new language to many scientific studies. Given our great ignorance of detailed structure and function in living systems, we need new analogies, new mental pictures, to try to rationalise what is happening. The nerves of the body, for instance, were at one time pneumatic channels; then they became a sort of telephone exchange when our technology had moved on a bit. Today, with much more detailed knowledge of ion transport across nerve membranes, there is a view of the nerve pulse as a soliton – a little bit of wave energy that has definite particle properties. There seems to be a similar on-off logic to computers in that the voltage in the nerve-cell body either reaches a certain level to fire a pulse, or it doesn't. Groups of neurons thus form particular binary patterns, so constituting "program" modules for the physical control of muscles. However, one should add that this view of a minimum threshold is now being challenged, there being new evidence that all inputs to the nerve cell body are faithfully reproduced in the axon signal.

These mental pictures can be very helpful, but should be used with discretion. Materialists tend to make excessive claims about computer systems, and some would have us believe that this technology is the ultimate justification of the reductionist approach. Just as the computer circuits give a totally determinate response to various stimuli, so do the neural networks. Through modern programming methods, they point out that computers and brains perform analogous functions. Even though computer methods currently involve sequential logic (one step at a time), we are now beginning to experiment with forms of parallel processing that the brain uses. This provides so much more flexibility and power, particularly in assessing images. Thus it is conceived that, as technology progresses, our robots will be designed more like brains, and brain processes will be understood in more robotic terms.

There was once great optimism for *Artificial Intelligence*, but this now seems to have run its course without any new light being shed on our mental processes. It was hoped that, through sophisticated programming techniques, and translating the rules of syntax into software logic, it would be possible to have an intelligent conversation with a computer system. Alan Turing provided the challenge: if we could not tell the difference between talking to a computer and another human being, then we would have to say that the computer was intelligent. But the *AI* experts never got anywhere near this. Some of us thought the whole experiment was pointless in the first place. The best that can be done is to transfer artificially some little aspect of our own intelligence to the software program, and which is in fact what happens in normal scientific programming. But no one has ever believed the machine had its own mathematical insight.

Those of a more mystical disposition can argue that computer analogies lead us to very different lines of thought. In energy terms, there are two quite distinct levels which are certainly suggestive of mind and body. There is the hardware circuitry sustained by certain electrical voltage levels; and there is the "immaterial" software coding which only changes the binary states within the hardware. Software is the ghost in the machine; and without it, the machine would be capable of nothing.

Pressing on with such an analogy, one can also say that such systems do not come about by accident. At every level, they are designed down to the last detail. Through the natural imaging abilities of certain gifted people, most structural and functional details can be thought through before anything tangible exists. Insight and logic – not chance and probability – carefully guide the whole process. If systems are intelligently conceived at a basic level, they have the capacity to develop to higher levels of operation. A good design will evolve, but a bad one will not. All that is suggestive of a *creative* evolution, not a *chance* one.

Given the good fortune to work on one of the most interesting projects in the early days of computer development, rather different thoughts became significant to me. By much trial and error, I slowly began to appreciate some of the real problems of designing a complex system, and assembling all the pieces together to form an integrated whole. For me, the most basic factor of all, and one appreciated now by all software designers, is that complexity and diversity is most easily achieved through "modular" structures. Each module, or subsystem, needs to be clearly defined, to be relatively independent, reasonably simple, and yet able to be used in different ways by other modules. A little calculation will show, for example, that if there are 10 modules, each able to interconnect with another module in 4 different ways, the number of *mode*s of running the whole system runs into billions. To try to obtain these billions of modes with a single module would be quite beyond the mind of man. Yet to construct much lesser systems, and limit their connectivities to just a few operations, one has a manageable task. It is the initial modular design, rather than clever circuitry and programming, that decides the power and usefulness of a system.

There are also simple practical reasons for proceeding along these lines. If the system is modular, one can individually test each module and its connective functions, and then systematically put it all together without getting hopelessly lost in the detail. Also, if intelligently designed, one can modify a selected module without losing the whole system. But if the system is created as a single entity – not modular – then it may be almost impossible to put together, or to operate it.

Within the software world, there are many examples of projects with fairly hopeless initial design that, after the spending of many millions of pounds, inevitably had to be abandoned. While most of the very early systems were designed and coded by individual people, major companies later took the view that if they put a hundred or so clever people together, they would be able to develop superior systems. But such people are extremely difficult to control, and disinclined to adhere to any specific design structure. As with musical composition, the best systems are conceived by a single human mind who directs all operations.

What is very clear to me in these advanced electronic systems, and learnt from hard experience, is that reductionist attitudes are of no use to the designer, or to those who would seek to understand the design. A successful modern system will be an amalgam of modules and subsystems, and simply cannot be understood in semi-conductor terms – just as we are never likely to understand Man in terms of genes or neurons. There are many quite different levels of logic, some relating to basic hardware, some to operating systems and languages, some to mathematical functions, some to printers and VDUs, some to the man-machine interface. Each level has its own modular organisation, and the logic is worked out according to the rules of that particular level.

Another way of expressing this is that there is no one part, or one module, or one component, or one program, that holds the secret to the whole system. Within the scientific community, there is this strong "lo-hereing-and-thereing" tendency. Look, they say, it's all in the genes, its all in the neurons, its all in the chemical transmitters. The secret of life is always supposed to be in one specific place. This is the very essence of reductionism. But a complex system may break down for a multitude of reasons; and for it to function as intended by the designer, all the problems have to be solved at all levels.

That said, there will always be an order of importance in any well-designed system. Each module will have a natural place in the hierarchical structure, from the man-machine interface, to the problem-solving mathematics and executive control software, down to the circuit board components. This is surely paralleled in the human being, from conscious mind, to autonomic nerve and hormone controls, to muscle and bone movement. The hierarchy defines the order of importance. Some things are more critical than others. We can break odd bones or strain muscles without serious long-term damage. But loss of spinal nerves or hormone centres is far more serious; and without the conscious mind, we are totally helpless. All very similar to modern electronic systems.

Those who have never been involved in technological design might reasonably wonder how representative my view is. There is certainly an impression around that the more one is involved in this type of work, the more machine-like one becomes. This may, unfortunately, apply to those who have to use and operate machines in routine and standardised ways. But for those who design, imagination, or imaging, is at the very core of the work, and this owes nothing to reductionist thought. If one took that seriously, and really believed there was no independent will, there would be no point in even trying to design something original. Modern electronic systems offer us a glimpse into the secrets of our own structure, and make us even more aware of the mysteries of the mind.

Unfortunately, the more one makes such arguments, the more extreme the claims of materialists, who now suggest that consciousness will be understood as an aspect of neural complexity. They even speculate that, one day, machines will have this property as they approach comparable levels of complexity. For most of us, I think that the notion of a *conscious* machine, a set of material components sitting in a box thinking about itself, and devising theories about its origin and function, is quite beyond belief.

In a recent and very typical reductionist book, *Neuronal Man – The Biology of Mind*, by Jean-Pierre Changeux, there are apparently no limits whatsoever to the power of biochemical reductionism. A reviewer tells us that '*he assaults dualist notions of a separate mind and spirit, the province of the philosopher and theologian, like a latter-day knight errant riding through a land of misguided heathens*'. We read on expectantly towards new revelations - only to find that we are destroying our brains with tranquilizers. Seven million packets a month are sold in France, he complains on the last page. One wonders why he is so surprised that the brain cannot take care of itself.

Like all such authors who abhor any suggestion of dualism, he simply cannot avoid it in general discussion. What "we" do to our brains is an important matter to him. "We" ought to be wiser, and take care of the way we treat our brains, just as we take care of our bodies. It is so difficult to conceive of the neural networks taking care of themselves, even for the most committed materialist. One would have to assume that the networks are conscious to the extent that they can decide what is best for them. But the "we" implies that there is some decision-making entity separate from the chemical brain. Clearly, it is more than a little difficult talking about what a brain does to itself.

At the time of buying this particular book, I also picked up another, William Barrett's *Death of the Soul*, which points in the opposite direction. The title is not quite right in that, while it traces philosophical thought from Descartes to modern times, and the slow elimination of the soul concept from Western thought, he points out that, in our abstract theorising and computer modelling, we are missing all that is obvious. How can we begin to discuss the conscious self and creative mind, the experience of joy and sadness, the sense of history and nostalgia, in biochemical or neuronal or semi-conductor terms? Science does not possess the vocabulary for all those things that are most real to us.

Reductionist methods have their obvious place in specialised scientific studies. But in advanced systems, it is the integration of the various levels of control that is so vital - *synthesis* rather than analysis. The case being suggested is essentially a pluralist one, in that, just as our most successful technological systems have to be built up with modular structures at several different levels, so to obtain the almost infinite complexity and flexibility of the human organism, one would expect, and indeed finds, an analogous structural design in living systems, only with many more modules, and vastly more interconnections.

The materialist position has perhaps been a little weakened by the latest findings of the Human Genome Project. The fact that there are only 30,000 human genes rather than 100,000 assumed for so many years, and that these are almost the same in many animals, can only indicate we are not exclusively determined by our genes. Nurture, we are now assured, plays a significant part in development. To those like Charles Darwin, who always maintained there was little to choose between humans and the higher primates, there is no great problem, much of our everyday behaviour being below the conscious level, and many automated responses we share with the animal world. But it is difficult to sustain the argument that conscious scientific analysis, and the development of new theories, is also part of the autonomic mechanisms. There is within us an integrative entity that can view the body with complete detachment, and is capable of creating its own conceptual world.

In our mentality - which has apparently arisen spontaneously in the last few moments of evolutionary time - we are light years ahead of any other organism. Externally, we have transformed the earth, creating cities and civilisations; internally we compose symphonies and formulate predictive mathematical theories. It becomes increasingly difficult to relate our remarkable mental abilities to anything genetic. At our best, we think seriously about purpose and meaning, and try to assess the human and social consequences of our work. In this, science as yet provides no guidance, and we each have to find our own path.

Slowly, in ways indicated above, and through an innate desire to consider the serious purposes of life, the concept of the soul, as distinct from the body, is slowly entering our vocabulary again. A forbidden word for much of the twentieth century, scientists used it at their peril. Throughout that period, Darwinians tried very hard to free us from archaic Platonic philosophy, but they have nothing to put in its place. It is difficult to envisage any genetic explanation of these higher conscious facilities, for without them, we could not begin to theorise about genetics in the first place. If the brain circuitry is pre-programmed, then what appears as rational enquiry is inevitable and pre-determined.

Even the most materialist scientist has to admit that, in his theorising about nature and the universe, it is necessary to assume that scientific knowledge is totally dependent on the notion that each researcher is *free* to decide which direction to take, and to choose between alternative theoretical formulations. This is an innate sense; and if this were not so, then research would be meaningless. Therefore it is helpful to have a word that encapsulates a process that is above, and free from, our genetic constitution.

During the 1990s, a few senior hard-line materialists set out on a crusade to eliminate all heretical thinking and thinkers from the scientific community. Anything outside their belief system was irrational, and not worthy of study. Listening to them, they obviously believed that rationality was their special preserve, and those outside science were incapable of following their levels of logic. Ignoring all the warnings about the dangers to science itself of such a fundamentalist course, they created a climate of fear, making it difficult for ordinary scientists to speak freely about their own personal beliefs.

I suspect their time is over. There is now a realisation that we bring to science the ethics and morals of our own cultural traditions. Science does not in any way provide these. The twentieth century began with such new optimism, but succeeded in becoming the most barbaric in all history. Scientists lost their moral compass. Terrible weapons of mass destruction were produced, and terrible experiments were performed on humans in the name of progress. The scientific endeavour lost the open-minded rational spirit of former centuries.

It is not surprising that many of those who have contributed most, such as Newton, Pascal, Faraday, Maxwell, Tesla, were of serious religious disposition. Materialists have always tried to explain away the "irrational" beliefs of such men. But in fact, it is these pioneers who were the genuine open-minded rationalists, accepting nature as it was, and being content just to explore the handiwork of a Creator, rather than impose on others a very limited human view of it.

Sir Isaac Newton, in particular, has been the subject of special vitriol during the second half of the twentieth century, from Jacob Bronowski to Stephen Hawking. In Newton's own times, there were people who wrote of this dark and devious person in Trinity College who was propagating the absurd idea that the sun was ninety-three million miles away. Nasty and treacherous are some of the adjectives now used. Certainly, like a number of other academics of the time, Newton had great problems with the intensely secretive Flamsteed, the astronomer royal, who wished to claim the prize for solving the longitude problem. Newton's public service at the Mint, and designing a new coinage to prevent counterfeiting, has even been used against him.

His experiments in alchemy, his mystical interests, his theological writings, his strong Protestantism, his problems with certain academics, his bachelor status, his relationship with his mother who remarried - these matters have all been extensively trawled over, and his thoughtful and retiring personality pulled apart by modern scientists and psychologists. While no one will ever do more for science, I have sometimes heard it said that he could not be considered a true scientist!

It would seem that Newton was never really comfortable with university life, and gradually relinquished his ties after a serious illness when he was fifty. He did not accept the doctrine of the Trinity, and, against the tradition of the time, did not take holy orders. He made it clear that he was far more at home among the Stamford farmers than the Cambridge parsons. Some of us find this rather refreshing. To get a more balanced view of Newton's life, academics would be well advised to study the published correspondence rather than modern biographies.

Interested in all knowledge, he realised only too well the dangers of writing a work like the *Principia* which dealt with basic mechanical principles. He feared, quite rightly, that such a work would be used to undermine traditional beliefs. That is why he was so reluctant to make it public, that is why he wrote in Latin and used forms of geometrical argument that few would understand. These are not the actions of a nasty man.

I believe that many scientists have greatly misunderstood Newton's life and philosophy over the last century, and this is a suitable time for re-examination. He is seen as a divided personality, doing remarkable mathematical work, and having nonsense ideas about much else. If one looks sensibly at his experiments in alchemy, we see him trying to understand the active forces in nature, and paving the way for what we now call chemistry. Biological systems were part of this alchemical interest, and he speculates in quite modern electrical terms about the major nerve pathways, and the control of muscles. The *ether*, both inside and outside material bodies, and possible cause of gravitation, continually fascinates him; and with his view of light as having both wave and particle characteristics, he comes close to modern thinking.

All this is within the framework of a Creator, who seems to intervene from time to time to create the solar system, or the human eye and brain. To Newton, it was inconceivable that such amazing material systems could have happened by accident. Always wanting to understand more about the Creator, he studied with great diligence the ancient philosophies and the most difficult parts of the bible. I would suggest that, far from a series of disparate interests, there is a single body of thought running through all his work.

To get a feel for the breadth of vision, utterly unlike any other, the simplest way is to read the last section of his *Opticks*, in which he comments extensively on his own queries about the nature of light, matter, life, ether, and the universe. These are careful discussions about what we know, what we don't, and with suggestions about how we might proceed. One could say that it mapped out the content of science for the next few hundred years. Through it all was his belief that nature is consistent, conformable, and deep down, simple.

To Newton, the active electrical energies are the key to understanding living systems. In his notes for the second edition of the *Principia,* there is the following passage:

'Unless I am wrong, it will first be necessary to understand the soul, and investigate the laws which he observes in these operations of the spirit, the powers and actions of the electrical spirit which pervades all bodies.'

This is very much the subject of twenty-first century science.

Chapter Two

Our Electromagnetic Body

From my study window, I observe this wonderful panorama of natural life with forms of infinite diversity and complexity. If our present science could explain how just a few of the relatively simpler forms come into being, what guides the cells into specific processes and positions to make roots and leaves and petals all harmoniously organised into a living whole, then perhaps I would have a little more respect for its rather extravagant claims.

Billions have been spent in research laboratories throughout the world taking the fruit-fly to bits, studying its genes and chromosomes, making chemical rearrangements to see what changes and deformities can be induced - and yet we are little the wiser. I know that there is a certain modern biological view that nothing of this nature is any sort of problem - given millions of years of development, organisms as complex as an elephant just happen to be the final way molecules organise themselves over time. Thus there is nothing much to study. But to those brought up in the physical sciences, with concepts of energy and force and field, the problems of biological structure remain a great challenge.

So from a biochemical or genetic or cellular viewpoint, we need to appreciate that there is little *causal* understanding of growth and form - as distinct from basic observation and categorisation. Biochemists and geneticists can argue that with our knowledge of the DNA structures in the nucleus of a cell, we now have an understanding, albeit incomplete, of how amino acids and proteins are synthesised in the cell; and perhaps in time we will move on to more complex units of tissues and organs and complete body systems. But as things stand today, the new

18

biochemistry has taken us only a little way further forward from Mendel in understanding the mechanisms of organic growth and form. As yet, we do not begin to understand the overall development of any living entity. The organisation into cell types, into specific organ and bone structures, into nerve and hormone control systems – these all remain a great mystery. We cannot understand the geometry of the most primitive forms of life. Chemistry simply doesn't deal with physical structure at these levels.

I much sympathise with that lone researcher, D'Arcy Thompson, who against all established opinion, pointed out that chemistry and genetics could never lead, of itself, to any understanding of geometrical form. Just how would one include most obvious matters of shape, structure, strength, currents, fields, plasticity, organisation, control, to name but a few relevant matters. In its current form, the human genome studies concern only chemical action. Geometry, mechanics, electromagnetics, control theory - these all belong to different orders of understanding.

Looking at the problem of organic form from a mathematical or common-sense viewpoint, there has to be a structural field of energy that, at the microscopic level, organises the molecular units into individual cells, and then at higher levels, guides the cells into major systems and a coherent whole. Such a view can be seen as complementary to attempts by geneticists and biochemists to work upwards from the molecular level. There may of course be a correspondence between the very large and very small, in that one might eventually find that the overall field pattern is related in some curious way to the bonding energies of the genes and chromosomes.

A rather vague concept of a morphogenetic field has been around in embryology for a long time, but not in any explicit *energetic* way that would be appreciated by physical scientists. It should be remembered that different cells in different positions have different functions, and it is difficult to avoid the assumption of some external or whole-body influence activating or inhibiting individual genes according to cell type and position. That there exists an overall electromagnetic influence is not an issue. The whole planet is conditioned by a magnetic shield and radiation belts, and we exist within this electromagnetic envelope. This shield produces daily or circadian rhythms in the environment, and we are now aware how these rhythms are reflected in the bodily processes, from hormone production to blood counts to nerve action.

A few embryologists, including Joseph Needham, have suggested some integrating *biofield* on the lines of nineteenth-century field theory; and prior to the modern DNA era, there were some tentative electrical theories of organic development. Needham, probably the greatest scholar of the twentieth century, had immense admiration for Clerk Maxwell; but although very influential, was unable to convey this enthusiasm to his biologist colleagues.

The first person to give real substance to such ideas was Professor Harold Saxton Burr of Yale University who, over about forty years, produced nearly a hundred scientific papers related to an *electrodynamic* theory of life. After developing a sufficiently sensitive voltmeter to measure electrical potentials around living systems, without taking current from them, he investigated many forms of life from seeds to trees to humans. Some of his work links in directly with the later work of Dubrov, noting for instance how lunar and solar cycles are reflected in plant physiology and human cycles. Other work on wound healing, involving strong positive potentials at the centre of an injury that attracted negative ions, was later developed by Nordenström with his electrical therapy for breast cancer. Robert Becker confirmed many of his measurements, and used electrical fields for regeneration of limbs in simple vertebrates. Burr eventually came to the conclusion that this overall field that he was measuring was far more than some by-product of chemical energy. It was in fact a guiding force matrix - one that integrated chemical reactions, and responded to the environmental rhythms. Although this was only DC experimentation, it did much to encourage the more difficult studies of oscillatory and magnetic effects of the nerves and cell membranes.

At a detailed internal level, the first thing to realise is the truly amazing complexity of the electrical activity of the whole body. In fact, each cell itself is so very remarkable, with billions of charged particles or ions, protein production and energy storage in the outer cytoplasm, and the orderly input and output of ions controlled through the protein channels in the outer cell membrane. The majority of cell types have a nucleus, each with a three-billion-base genetic program and materials to form all the required proteins. The outer membrane, with its natural sensitivity to audio-frequency potentials and waves, is one of nature's most remarkable constructs. All the trillions of cells of the body, not only the nerve cells, are involved in this fantastic electrical activity, making it vastly more complex than any engineered system. As the psalmist says, '*I am fearfully and wonderfully made*'.

Overall control comes from the brain and major pathways of the nervous system - the brainstem, the spinal cord, and two chains of autonomic nerves running parallel to the cord. Attached to the brainstem are twelve cranial nerves affecting the head and internal organs; and attached to the spinal cord are thirty-one spinal nerves controlling the trunk and the limbs (figure 2b).

To make any progress with energy modelling of the overall structure, we obviously have to consider these major electrical pathways. Individually, the nerves create pulses or wavelets or solitons - comparatively slow-moving packets of oscillatory energy - and at a frequency governed partly by intrinsic resonances within the nervous system, and partly by the needs of the moment from the surrounding environment. Another way of expressing this is that all systems have an idling mode, and an active mode.

At any time within the central channel, the overall electrical effect is a significant current flow. Thus, from basic electromagnetics, we know that there will be a magnetic field coiling around the spine, and an electrical field parallel to the current movement. Naturally there will be lesser fields around the individual spinal, cranial, and autonomic nerves. In terms of the movement of individual ions, which are generally at right angles to the current or pulse flow, these also create magnetic and electrical field effects according to standard theory. However, as these involve positive sodium ions one way, and positive potassium ions the other, the combined field effect will be extremely small.

Whether it is reasonable to use the term *electromagnetic body*, that is somewhat debatable. Most biologists seem to believe that electromagnetic effects are simply the *result* of moving ions in the body, and represent only a residuum of energy. However, those who have studied classical electromagnetics are not likely to take this one-sided view, regarding matter and field as mutually interdependent. An obvious example is a tuned circuit in which a magnetic field comes into play, and which then drives the current backwards and forwards. The field is an active agent; and without it, there would be no oscillation. Similarly, I would suggest that the fields of the body are *active* energies.

The substitution of *system* for *body* would perhaps be less controversial. *Body* is a rather more challenging term reminiscent of Indian philosophy, and suggesting some distinctive closed entity. In the Eastern view, which increasingly interests Western academics, the human organism is an amalgam of bodies, from the lowest material level of atoms and molecules and cells, to the highest mental functions. Between are various intermediary systems, including the electrical life-forces that pervade and sustain the material system. This has been translated by various Western movements as an *etheric* or *subtle* body, terms which orthodox scientists get rather emotional about, and which tend to make for problems where none essentially exist.

By and large I am inclined to side with orthodoxy on this matter because there is not much point talking about *subtle energy* if you cannot relate it to known energies. Those who insist on the term tell me that it is much *more subtle* than electromagnetism; and when I respond that electromagnetic fields can be as subtle as you choose them to be, right down to infinitesimal strengths, they insist it must be a different form of energy. But even assuming this is so - a form of negative energy, or some level not yet explored - it will surely be *expressed* at the physical level in electromagnetic terms. With our present knowledge and technology, it is the only way we can study it.

Therefore, given that moving pulses and ions are always accompanied by electric and magnetic fields, and also that the bonding forces between atoms and molecules are electromagnetic in nature, there is little to disagree about concerning the active electrical forces in the body. Although not a completely closed system like the cellular body, it is relatively closed, the fields being just measurable a few centimetres from the skin. Thus it would seem reasonable to talk about an *electromagnetic body of forces*.

This to me is the most natural of ideas; and the orthodox assumption that the body is controlled by chemical action is extremely unnatural. Chemical action is essentially *disintegrative,* while electromagnetic fields, such as those of the earth, or the remarkable bonding forces holding the DNA together, are *integrative.* There is a simple choice between order and disorder. So many things make general sense with the concept of controlling biofield guiding the positions and actions of all the individual parts. Nothing makes any sense in terms of localised chemical action in trillions of cells.

Quite apart from any rationale about basic embryonic growth, there is the obvious matter of healing and regeneration, and which, from the work of Becker and others, we know to be influenced by fields and currents. On a purely chemical basis, it is a total mystery how skin and muscle and nerve can be repaired so perfectly, with all the requisite cells slotting into place again. But with an overall field guiding the whole process, it is no longer a mystery. Through the gentle action of these forces over days or weeks or months, new cells are suitably positioned, the blood supply is reorganised, and the nerves are reconnected with the main system. On this basis alone, I am convinced about an integrative electromagnetic mechanism. If biochemists want to call it *vitalism*, that is their problem. Considering all the evidence, I see it as a sensible rational conclusion.

Given our present anatomical and physiological knowledge of the main aspects of the nervous system, we need to expand this with much more specific electrical data. Many basic parameters have never been of interest to the life scientists who concentrate almost exclusively on the chemical aspects. First and foremost, we require much more data about the main frequencies in the nervous system - only in the overall brainwaves of the cortex has there been much interest in this aspect. Then, closely associated with this, we require careful analysis of conduction speeds which vary considerably from the spinal cord to the peripheral nerves. And beyond that, we must analyse field strengths and energy dispersion. These are the basic ingredients for any modelling of the electromagnetic body.

From a general mathematical viewpoint, the problem is to find a field pattern that at the cellular level is sufficiently complex and variable, while at the same time possessing an overall coherence for the growth of major systems. This could only possibly be achieved by an oscillatory system involving a variety of frequencies continually in and out of phase with each other. Even a single frequency source, suitably constrained, can achieve quite complex patterning, as Chladni demonstrated with sand sprinkled on to a vibrating plate. Similarly Hans Jenny has generated beautifully detailed 3-dimensional forms with a variety of materials using a single initiating frequency in the audio range. Spirographs - equivalent to two or more frequencies - also demonstrate this patterning process.

In Jenny's *cymatic* experiments, stationary waves are set up - such as occur in organ pipes or violin strings. This is in contrast to "free" waves that radiate out in all directions. Stationary waves involve energies that are constrained by matter or other energy fields. They generate harmonics that interact with each other in complex ways. And in losing their freedom and homogeneity, they are forced into localised patterning processes.

Towards the end of his rather short life, the distinguished mathematician Alan Turing made the suggestion that the patterning processes of organic systems were caused by chemical stationary waves, and postulated the existence of *morphogens* that supposedly controlled these processes. He made the first attempts to model this by computer simulation, but his sudden death brought this work to an end.

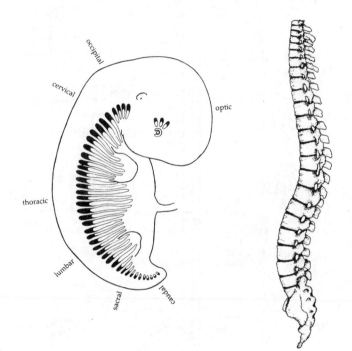

Figure 2a Embryonic somites and adult spine

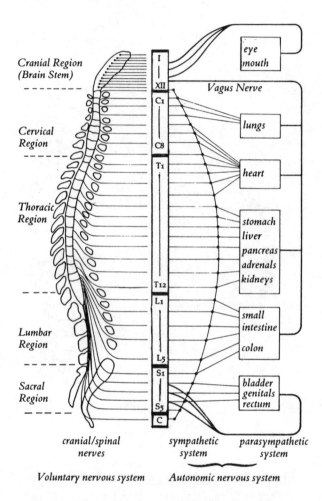

Figure 2b The human nervous system with 12 cranial nerves and 31 spinal nerves. The voluntary system controls muscles and movement, and the autonomic system looks after the internal processes. There are two sympathetic chains of neurons on either side of the spine that activate organs, while specific parasympathetic nerves regulate organs.

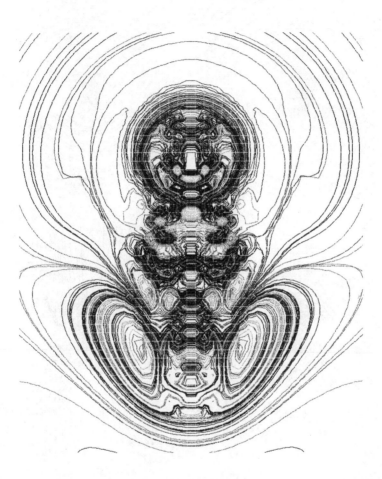

Figure 2c Typical contours of electrical potential using 46 oscillators. Several pictures are superimposed to follow the wave progression.

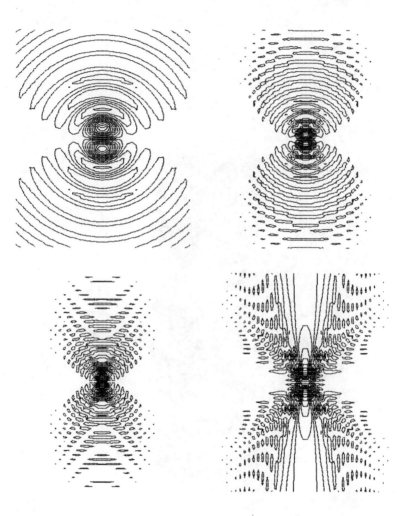

Figure 2d Effects of conduction speed on oscillating electrical dipole. The first picture is the standard electrical field; the next three show the effect of reducing the speed, with a break-up into small cellular elements.

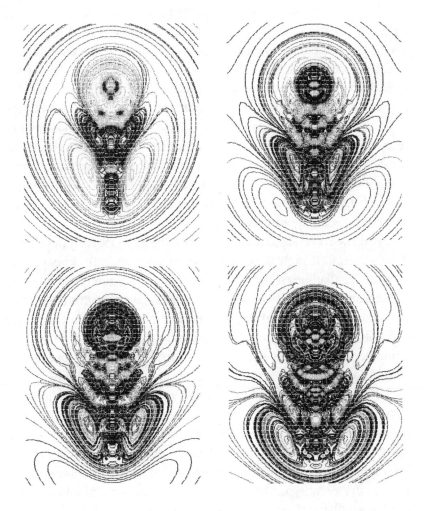

Figure 2e Contours of electrical potential, using 46 oscillators. The different patterns show the effect of decreasing the conduction speed, or increasing the size.

Thanks to the new superconducting SQUID magnetometers, we can now measure the magnetic component around the body. This was first done by David Cohen in the 1970s, and fully recorded in the American journal *Physics Today*. To screen out the earth's field, two compensating magnetometers were used. The intensity is greatest near the chest, being about one millionth of the earth's field, and frequencies up to about 500 cycles per second (Hz) were recorded there. Around the head where the field is over a hundred times smaller, the magnetic patterns (MEG) correspond very closely with the electrical patterns of the EEG. These magnetic methods have been used successfully to obtain precise information about the focus of epileptic seizures.

In my own private research in this area, the idea gradually developed in my mind that it might be possible to generate a suitable morphogenetic field by postulating a series of oscillators along the cerebrospinal axis, each creating some form of stationary wave. Assuming this is the case, one can calculate the cumulative energy potential term for all the oscillators at each point of a surrounding grid, and from which equipotential contours can be drawn. As a minimum, such an exercise should demonstrate whether the idea had any possible validity.

Before embarking on this, it seemed sensible to study how the nervous system develops from the early embryological stages. The cerebrospinal axis, apart from being the primary control channel for the body, is also the principal line of development, with the major nerve, muscle, and bone systems emanating from it. The first suggestion of this channel in the embryo is the long tube of material interestingly called the *notochord*. Parallel to the notochord, the material folds back on itself to form the spinal cavity; and at discrete intervals along its length, segments of cellular material separate out to form the *somites*. In the human being, up to about 44 somites are eventually formed, to be followed by muscles and vertebrae, together with the 31 spinal nerves and 12 cranial nerves.

My own idiosyncratic view of this remarkable process is that the final vertebrate structure is reminiscent of a cello, with the brain and spinal cord bearing an unusual resemblance to the original sperm.

One thing that has always puzzled me is why there is nothing in conventional anatomy, physiology, and embryology that tries to account for the intricate segments within the spine. As an amateur observer, this segmentation, and all the variants between different animals, seem the essential key to vertebrate form. If we had just some slight rational insight into how all this came about, then we would have the beginnings of a theory of structure.

So of all embryological problems, it is the segmentation along the notochord that is probably the most fundamental. The beginning of this process is called *gastrulation*, occurring after the formation of the spherical structure called the *blastula*. One comparable process to the somite divisions is the segmentation of the DNA material into 46 chromosomal pieces as the cell is about to divide. It is possible that the segmentation of the somites, and of the DNA, could be achieved by similar vibrational energy processes.

In cymatics, form is a function of frequency; and with larger aggregates of matter, from molecules to cells to whole-body systems, the rate of vibration gets lower and lower. In setting up a possible model to reflect embryonic development, we need first some idea about the general range of frequencies, then something about relative frequency along the spinal axis, and lastly, if possible, a few specific frequencies. All of this we would expect to find reflected in the nervous system, or in the fields around the body.

Measurement of nerve frequency has never been a high priority in physiological research, and information is rather sparse. Maximum frequency is thought to be about 700 Hz (cycles per second), corresponding to a musical note of about F above top C. It cannot in fact be much higher than this, because the whole system is subject to a delay of one or two milliseconds at a synapse - the chemical junction between a nerve axon ending and other cells. Thus higher frequencies would be too fast to get any response. This can be easily demonstrated with a simple audio-frequency electrical oscillator. Frequencies above top F are hardly noticed; but as the frequency is reduced, tingling in the nervous system is experienced.

Pressure on the fingers, relating to the lower neck, is about 500 Hz, or close to top C. In the cerebral area, vibrations seem to be mostly in the 50-100 Hz range, and, as argued in *Mind, Body and Electromagnetism*, the EEG measurements on the outer skull, from about 30 Hz down to 2 in deep sleep, may represent *difference* or *beat* frequencies. From personal investigations on my own spine, the trunk seems to be most sensitive to vibrations in the two octaves below top C - about 125-500 Hz.

The major point to make, and one not often realised by scientists, is that the body, taken as a whole, is an audio-frequency system. It would in fact be nearer the mark if we confined the audio-frequencies to the *vocal* range. This range would seem to be about 50-700 Hz, which represents about four octaves. Another way of expressing this is that it contains 40-odd semitones. Is this just a coincidence, given the 40-odd somites, segments, nerves, chromosomes? Perhaps so; but when one looks at both the spinal and chromosome segmentation in a musical context, and with a geometrical eye (the semitone interval ratio is 15:16), there is reason for mathematicians to believe that this may be a promising line of enquiry.

Note that the natural mechanical resonances of the major physical systems have a similar range to the electrical frequencies. It is a special property of living systems that there is a close relationship between the physical and electrical forces, quite different from human machines. In the inert material of technological circuitry, the speed of conduction approaches that of light waves, and the frequency range extends to millions of cycles per second. But in our own bodies, the conduction speeds of nerve pulses are unusually slow, with a range of about 1 - 130 metres per second, depending mainly on the axon diameter, and whether or not the axons have myelin sheathing. And as previously stated, the synaptic delay at each nerve junction slows things up even more. It takes just a simple division sum to see that, with a typical conduction speed of 10 metres per second and a frequency of 500 Hz, there would be a wavelength of 2 centimetres.

Such a length gives us the right scale of patterning in the adult spine, and points towards what might be called the *modular vibrational* approach to spinal activity. Many bodily functions and responses are controlled at the vertebral level rather than through transmission circuits to the brain. With a major nerve junction above and below, each vertebral section can be thought of as the source of an electrochemical oscillation with its own distinctive resonant frequency. Thus in total, we might consider the *idling* state of the spine as a set of standing waves arranged in some orderly sequence of frequency. All this activity would generate most of the energy of the overall electromagnetic field – other parts of the nervous system being much less significant, especially in the embryonic stages.

Formulating a theoretical model, the mathematical representation of a set of standing waves is no problem. As for the actual frequency sequence, it is not difficult to make an intelligent guess from the general geometry of the human spine, and the limited experimental evidence. More of a potential problem is how this energy falls away from the source through the surrounding cellular material. However, we know that natural fields tend to have *dipole* characteristics, these arising from oppositely polarised sources close together, and rapidly dispersing. Considering EEG and other physiological evidence in terms of classical electromagnetics, Paul Nunez has argued in a scholarly work that the nerve structures of the brain, and also the axon currents of the spinal cord, do in fact create dipole fields.

My attempts to model the fields are much simpler, mathematically, than the efforts of either Paul Nunez or Alan Turing. This is partly a difference of view about the processes we are trying to understand. Alan Turing, for instance, tried to model natural chemical diffusion processes, and to follow the patterning effects. To me, the structures of the human organism are so highly defined that it requires a very specific oscillatory organisation controlling the whole development from the outset. My own relatively simple approach is to consider each spinal segment, or somite, as a dipole source of electromagnetic energy, and calculate through a computer program the cumulative electrical potential at each point of a surrounding grid.

For a static or non-oscillatory dipole, the field varies as the inverse cube of the distance, and the potential as the inverse square. For an oscillating dipole, there are three field components: a *near* field as the inverse cube, an *induction* field as the inverse square, and a *radiation* field as the inverse distance. The corresponding potential term has two components: inverse distance, and inverse square. All these components are also dependent on frequency and transmission speed. This makes for more complication, but such matters are easily expressed with modern programming methods.

The general form of the embryonic model is based on the currents along the primitive spine or notochord, and the magnetic forces naturally encircle it according to the basic laws of electromagnetism. The electrical field is at right angles to the magnetic, and essentially parallel to the notochord. These two together create a physical or mechanical effect that is radial - at right angles to both. All the components are oscillatory, and changing direction according to the different wave effects at different positions and times.

The effect of the velocity of conduction on an oscillating electrical dipole is of considerable interest. In figure 2d, the first picture uses a comparatively high conduction velocity, and generates the standard electrical contours that can be found in basic textbooks on the subject. Then, as we reduce the velocity, rather unexpected things begin to happen. As can be seen, the contours begin to break up into smaller and smaller *cellular* units, which is of course the sort of detail we find in actual organic systems. Of all the computer experiments that I have carried out, this one interests me as much as any, being derived entirely from orthodox electromagnetic theory. Certainly I have not found any textbooks that discuss this phenomenon.

With position, frequency, and dispersion roughly defined, and an awareness of the significance of conduction speed, there is something to experiment with, and a computer program can generate the equipotential electrical contours. The resulting patterns then allow us to assess whether the model has any possible validity. The pictures shown in figures 2c and 2e are typical of the type of patterning one gets from such a theoretical model, and were obtained with surprisingly little trial and error. Clearly they have some of the characteristics we are looking for.

The actual model is precisely defined in the *Ross Language* system, and its development is discussed in *Mind, Body and Electromagnetism*. The function used for defining electric potential is approximately dipole in character, and the frequency ratio between adjacent oscillators corresponds to a semitone interval. There are 31 oscillators of increasing frequency from the base of the spine to the neck, and corresponding to the spinal nerves. These are followed by another increasing sequence of 15 lower frequency ones from the brainstem to the cortex. The speed of conduction is assumed to increase as the square of the distance from the centre - roughly corresponding with experimental data indicating an increase from spine to periphery of about 1 to 100 metres per second.

To give an averaged effect over a small period of time, and so to highlight any consistent patterning, several component contour maps are superimposed to generate the overall picture. With higher conduction speeds or smaller dimensions, the contouring gives a closed cellular effect, but with some suggestion of the further development. For lower speeds or larger dimensions, there is an opening up of the head and pelvic formations, and with very variable patterns in between. And as already noted, the finer details indicate small cellular elements.

Naturally, one cannot assert that the various assumptions made are directly validated by the pictures. But in conjunction with our newly developing knowledge of the cell membrane, and its unusual sensitivity to extremely weak low-frequency fields, there is added plausibility to this approach. This sensitivity, existing only in the narrow temperature range of the body, is now being referred to as *biosuperconductivity*, and is connected with the protein channels embedded in the cell membrane. Some, particularly Alexander Dubrov, have gone on to suggest that the low-frequency resonances between the Earth's surface and the ionosphere are continually recharging living systems, and also that the geomagnetic field in general has an important bearing on the polarisation of molecules and genes at the beginning of life.

For professional students of embryology, this mathematical approach to morphogenesis can be seen as a natural extension of the theory of gradients proposed by Child, and of associated concepts of head and trunk organisers much discussed in the 1930s. Child's theory involved the notion of an axial gradient from head to tail, and from axis to periphery, the gradient being based on metabolic rates or oxidation. While the general idea of an *activity-gradient* came to be accepted, the question of whether this was related directly to metabolism remained controversial. Various alternative physical, chemical, and electrical hypotheses were put forward, but experimental objections were found to all. In the pre-computer age, it was of course impossible to develop theoretically any such hypothesis to a meaningful level. The calculations for the pictures in this chapter, for instance, would take years of hand calculation as compared with the few seconds by our fastest machines.

In the 2-dimensional model used, each source of oscillatory energy is radial, so generating the overall bilateral symmetry. The combined effect is a high gradient along the spinal axis, and also perpendicular to the axis from each source. This would suggest that the major elements of the nervous system do follow the lines of high electrical intensity. Opponents of any specifically *electrical* theory of gradients have always pointed out that nerve axons often develop right next to each other in the opposite direction – this objection being based on the assumption that the field is constantly polarised in one direction only. But with oscillatory fields, one would expect that axons could grow either way. More generally, when one considers the ceaseless change of electric and magnetic waves throughout the organism, together with the unique sensitivities of membrane structure, then many of the older objections to electrical gradient theory cannot be sustained.

To develop the electromagnetic hypothesis theoretically, there are many possible lines to pursue. Continuing just with the 2-dimensional model, we should be able to determine, for a given potential function, what sort of grouping of oscillators and frequencies are required for the initial development of a limb bud. We could investigate Spemann's experiments concerning the dominance of head and trunk organisers on the assumption that each organiser is a particular subset of the cerebrospinal centres. In three dimensions, the most obvious morphological characteristics to consider are the asymmetries in the internal organs, and from front to back of the body.

For the physical scientist, perhaps the most challenging exercise is the analysis of the force patterns in the very first stages of growth from the fertilized egg. Using Maxwell's equations, we can determine the physical forces on the cell surface; and by using computational techniques similar to those of finite-element analysis, it may be possible to model the external organisation for a few cell divisions.

Experimentally, the electromagnetic model may provide helpful suggestions for medical research. If valid, the model emphasises that, above all, frequency is the critical factor. But in so much experimentation, the specific frequency seems of little consequence. In one set of medical trials at some unspecified frequency, we hear that low-frequency energies have no effect; in other trials, that the physiological processes are considerably speeded up. Yet we know from a wide range of experiments that a change in frequency, even a very small change, can reverse or totally alter the nature of the response. For example, when subject to a flickering light, one may experience whirling discs of colour at 11 Hz, vivid memories at 18 Hz, and nothing in particular at 19 Hz. Electrical input of 100 volts may be lethal at 60 Hz, while thousands of volts are completely harmless at a higher frequency. In our medical research, it is important that we explore the natural resonances of each individual person; and by tuning in to the basic rhythms of the electromagnetic system, we might discover simpler and safer forms of treatment.

In my own research with a low-frequency oscillator, I have been hopeful of finding certain basic frequencies for energising or balancing the cerebro-spinal system. But with twenty years of experimentation on myself, I have become more and more aware of the complexities of assessing what might be helpful in therapy, and what damaging. Naturally I am happy that many others have had specific successes -

particularly wound and bone healing, and pain control in childbirth. The partial success of Dr Nordenström in the treatment of breast cancer was also encouraging, but disappointing in that it has not been developed further.

Recently, I have gone back to an idea suggested by my earliest experiments, and by others who have experimented with the effect of different musical notes on healthy and cancerous cells. Applying milliamp currents oscillating about lower or middle C to the upper part of the body through the hands, I have found that viral symptoms of colds and coughs seem to clear up rather quickly. In terms of mechanism, I can only assume that this frequency stimulates the immune system. Similar experimentation with frequencies about F and G does not seem to have this effect, and may make a condition worse. Although no more than anecdotal to medical men, in terms of the concept of an *electromagnetic body*, this is a rational idea. It is based on experiment, without psychosomatic content, and is well within purview of medical science.

On the larger scale, what is needed most of all today are maps of frequency and conduction velocity for the whole body - for the skin surface, the major organs, the bones, and the spinal and cranial nerves. This is a basic step in defining the *electromagnetic body*, and should provide a solid basis for new electrical and magnetic therapies. Compared with the billions of dollars and millions of man-hours spent on the Human Genome project, the construction of these maps would require only a fraction of such resources.

For those deeply involved in the complexities of cellular chemistry, this may be all too simplistic. Yet for those in the mathematical sciences, there will always be the belief in the existence of simple laws operating behind the scenes. All of nature, and much of technology is beyond understanding - until we appreciate the guiding principles. The solar system was an unintelligible maze of circles until Newton proposed the inverse square law of gravitation. A computer may appear to be extremely complex, but the essential design can be explained to anyone. The same is true of software: if we do not have an easily intelligible structure, we cannot develop the complexity within. To those who say that the concept of the *electromagnetic body* is too simple to account for the complexities of vertebrate systems, I would argue that the construction, operation, and evolution of intricate and detailed systems will depend on relatively simple formative principles. I would also argue that the frequency model proposed allows for the complexities we actually find in living organisms.

Chapter Three

Nikola Tesla

I have little doubt that, over the course of this new century, we will learn more and more about the remarkable life of Nikola Tesla, the extraordinary Serbian inventor who, in the title of a recent biography, is referred to as *The Man who invented the Twentieth Century*. Many would assume this must be a great exaggeration; but to those who have studied his contributions to world science and technology, it is close to the truth. If ever a man came from another planet to teach us new ways of harnessing energy for the benefit of all, it was Tesla.

Great technological progress ultimately depends on a few individual minds, not on large teams of people. There is much discussion today about the mysteries of the pyramids, and the seemingly high level of technological skill required for their construction. But if we think about Tesla's contributions to the twentieth century, we realise that it required only one really intelligent and inventive person to teach a civilisation how to construct a pyramid with perfectly proportioned stones aligned with such accuracy.

Tesla was born of Serbian parents in 1856 at Smiljan in Croatia, and went to school there and later at Gospic and Karlovac. His higher education was at Graz Polytechnic and Prague University. After a period with a telephone company in Budapest, he moved to Paris in 1882, joining the Continental Edison Company. From there he was invited to the USA in 1884 to work directly for Edison. This didn't work out as he hoped, and there followed a period digging ditches for two dollars an hour. In 1887 he obtained financial backing for his own company, and publicly demonstrated the AC motor the following year.

This was the beginning of a twenty-year period of remarkable innovation and research. From 1891 to 1896, he combined with George Westinghouse to build the first AC power station, involving dynamos, transformers, low-frequency transmission, motorised equipment, and lighting. After this he concentrated on higher frequency technology including wireless, radio-controlled machines, x-rays, earth conduction, ball-lightning, oscillators, electro-therapeutics, and many other matters. There was a gradual decline after World War I, partly because of lack of funds and partly through age. According to current evidence, 112 patents were issued to him in the USA, and 109 in other countries. He died in New York in 1943.

These are some basic facts of his life. To try to understand him at a personal level is probably as difficult as getting to the truth about Isaac Newton. Like Newton, he never married, and seemed content with the pursuit of knowledge for its own sake. He was exceptionally well-read, fluent in several languages, and had no problems with advanced mathematical methods in electromagnetism. He loved poetry, and in his youth committed long tracts to memory. Given this literary background, it is not surprising that, when in New York, he moved among a cultural élite that included Mark Twain and other writers. He was always elegant in appearance; and in later photographs there is something of the aristocrat in his bearing.

It would seem that he never particularly sought the company of scientists and academics, although he studied carefully matters related to his own work, and often publicly commented in considerable detail on new experimental findings of others. Through his upbringing and early school years, he was highly self-disciplined, and one wonders how that affected those that worked for him. But all the evidence suggests that, although demanding the highest standards of workmanship, his employees and co-workers on research projects were extremely loyal. The fact that he never created a fortune for himself (although creating great fortunes for many others), and lived very simply, must have commanded respect.

Whatever one says about Tesla, one finds almost the opposite in

Thomas Edison, the great home-spun trial-and-error inventor, combative, competitive, financially astute, and dismissive of fanciful theoretical methods. For creating direct current (DC) devices, Edison found that nothing much more than the simple Ohm's Law was ever required. Why should anyone want to be bothered with unnecessarily complicated things like alternating currents (AC) when DC provided the answers? Edison was making big money with it.

Clearly, being so dismissive of the attempts to use alternating current, Edison had little of interest to offer Tesla. And Tesla was upset by his American business methods, considering that Edison had defaulted on certain promised rewards. When the AC system began to challenge Edison financially, there was a major battle. But after a number of dirty tricks against Tesla, including making everyone aware that it was going to be used for the electric chair and therefore unsafe, he gave way to the superior system. Tesla even received the Edison Medal in 1917.

Before he arrived in America, Tesla had already solved many of the major problems of AC technology. He had been told in his student days that there was no solution to the problem of constructing a motor running directly on alternating current. The existing DC motor required a commutator to reverse the current every half-cycle, but this was neither reliable nor efficient, and there was much sparking on the commutator connections. Tesla reasoned that, as the rotary motion of dynamos naturally generated AC electricity, there should be some complementary process that produced rotary motion from AC. And if there was, it should be highly efficient, cutting out intermediate processes such as transforming the dynamo AC to DC.

Under AC, one could get the motor to rotate a little way; but then, as the current changed direction, together with the associated magnetic field, the rotational force was in the wrong direction. Tesla's solution was carefully explained and publicly demonstrated many years after conception. In its final form, it involved three-phase current: as one component current reversed direction, the next took over. It also involved a careful arrangement of angled coils to correspond with the different phases. His three-phase system and coil arrangements remain the standard today after more than a hundred years.

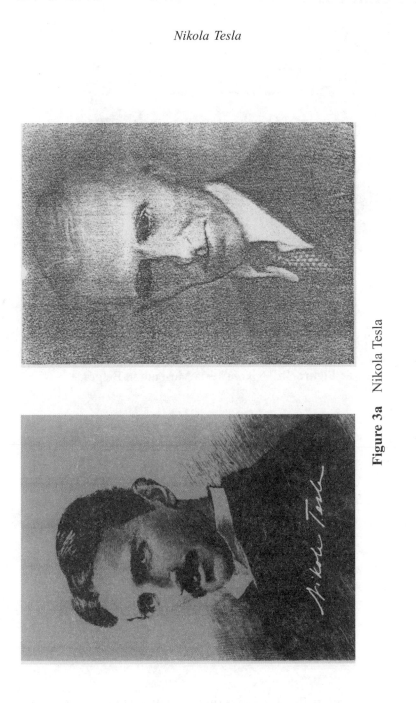

Figure 3a Nikola Tesla

Figure 3b   Nikola Tesla Museum in Belgrade

Figure 3c   Tesla experimenting with high voltages

Figure 3d   Colorado Springs temporary laboratory

Figure 3e   World Telegraphy tower

In his famous 1888 lecture and demonstration to the American Institute of Electrical Engineers, and which George Westinghouse attended, he shows step by step an arrangement that generates a magnetic field rotating with the motor, and thus applying a consistent torque. In his opening remarks, he sets the scene.

'In the presence of the existing diversity of opinion regarding the relative merits of the alternate and continuous current systems, great importance is attached to the question of whether alternate currents can be successfully used in the operation of motors.
…The subject which I now have the pleasure of bringing to your notice is a novel system of electrical distribution and transmission of power by means of alternate currents, affording peculiar advantages, particularly in the way of motors, which I am confident will at once establish the superior adaptability of these currents to the transmission of power and will show that many results heretofore unattainable can be reached by their use; results which are very much desired in the practical operation of such systems and which cannot be accomplished by means of continuous currents.'

This is the first official announcement to the world at large that Tesla had the basic answers for AC power, convincing his audience not only about the practicality of AC motors, but also about their very superior efficiency and reliability. From this, Tesla went on to work out all the details of a complete system of AC power, from power station generation, to transmission over long distances, and to the use of AC for lighting and motorised equipment. Edison's DC power stations had serious limitations, and to get any reasonable voltage, one had to live within about half-a-mile of the station. Many rich people with large estates bought their own DC power systems.

Using Tesla's designs and about forty of his patents, Westinghouse obtained the first contract for AC power, involving a hydroelectric system. What was done at Niagara Falls and the town of Buffalo by the Tesla-Westinghouse partnership quickly became the standard for power systems throughout the world. Although Buffalo was quite close by, the AC methods developed allowed electricity to be transmitted over large distance without significant loss of power. The actual transmission frequency of electricity we owe to Tesla. The prevailing opinion in his time was that it would have to transmitted at about 140 Hz (cycles per second), but Tesla was certain that a frequency around 60 Hz would be optimum. Again this remains the standard.

After this remarkable development, Tesla focused his attention on the concept of electrical resonance, and the development of tuned circuits. Many would consider this Tesla's major contribution to the modern world. Certainly the implications of an oscillatory and tunable device without moving parts are quite as far-reaching as the AC power generation, leading to the world of radio, television, computers, recorders, and in fact all methods of selective data communication.

The most basic tuned circuit consists two wires connecting a coil and a capacitor (a condenser in those days). As the current passes through the wires from the plate with a surplus of charge, a magnetic field is created in the coil which induces the current to surge forwards and charge up the other plate. This charge then surges backwards, and so an electrical wave is created. Precise frequencies are obtained by adjusting the capacitor and/or the coil, and electromagnetic theory gives us an exact formula for this.

Today, Tesla is considered by many specialists to be the inventor not only of the tuned circuit, but also of wireless technology - although others like Marconi were to commercialise it later. He took out twelve patents between 1897 and 1902 dealing with wireless communication. If there is any confusion about this issue, it is mainly because Tesla combined two distinctive ideas into his *wireless* concept, and the first patent in 1897 clearly stated both. He was interested in sending not only messages and data, but also transmitting power without wires. Given his expertise, the first was a straightforward development. But the second involved ideas difficult to establish in a confined laboratory, and required much new experimentation on a very large scale.

While designing the power station, he had begun to work on these more ambitious ideas for the transmission of power - not ones that would endear him to the power companies who saw almost unlimited profits for a long time to come with thousands of the existing Tesla-Westinghouse systems throughout the world. Tesla had studied transmission in rarefied gases and the atmosphere, and decided that, using much higher frequencies, he could probably do away with the wires, and send power to any part of the world. The Earth itself would be one side of the circuit, and the upper atmosphere (including what we now term the ionosphere) the other. Ideally, he wanted a transmitting system ten or more miles above the earth. But he reasoned that, with sufficiently high voltage, one could access the more rarified layers from a much lower level.

Such thoughts led on to the most remarkable series of experiments in the Colorado Desert in 1899, and lasting for about eight months. The implications of such experiments are, a hundred years later, just beginning to be understood. He and his team built a temporary laboratory (basically a very large shed) 2,000 metres above sea-level, mainly to see if, with the use of very high voltages and high frequencies. the upper atmosphere could usefully conduct significant quantities of electrical power over long distances.

Note that, in the context of 1899, these *high* frequencies were up to 30,000 Hz, very much lower than the high frequencies of millions or billions of cycles per second that we are familiar with today as part of the upper end of the electromagnetic spectrum. Tesla's high frequencies are within the long-wave band of radio frequencies.

As already indicated, Tesla had been thinking hard about such experiments for several years. In an 1893 lecture to the Franklin Institute, he had this to say.

'In connection with resonance effects and the problem of transmission of energy over a single conductor, I would say a few words on a subject which constantly fills my thoughts and

which concerns the welfare of all. I mean the transmission of intelligible signals or perhaps even power to any distance with or without wires. I am becoming daily more convinced of the practicability of the scheme; and though I know full well that the great majority of scientific men will not believe that such results can be practically and immediately realised, yet I think that all consider the developments in recent years by a number of workers to have been such as to encourage thought and experiment in this direction. My conviction has grown so strong that I no longer look upon this plan of energy or intelligence transmission as a mere theoretical possibility, but as a serious problem in electrical engineering, which must be carried out some day. ... We know that electric vibration may be transmitted through a single conductor. Why then not try to avail ourselves of the earth for this purpose? We need not be frightened by the idea of distance. To the weary wanderer counting the mile-posts, the earth may appear very large; but to that happiest of all men, the astronomer, who gazes at the heavens, and by their standard judges the magnitude of our globe, it appears very small. And so I think it must seem to the electrician, for when he considers the speed with which an electrical disturbance is propagated through the earth, all his ideas of distance must completely vanish.'

From the journal that he kept every day, we may surmise that the months at Colorado Springs were some of Tesla's happiest. He was entranced by the whole environment. He loved the purity and clarity of the atmosphere: the wheels and carriages of trains could be seen so clearly five miles away, and every little sound detected. The cloud formations were endlessly fascinating, and the sunsets unbelievable in their beauty. Others had obviously been well aware of all this for a long time, because he tells us that he was always meeting asthmatic sufferers who had come to live or holiday in those parts.

As for the actual experiments, they exceeded all expectations. Using frequencies of several thousand Hertz, and generating huge potentials up to a hundred million volts, he succeeded in lighting two hundred lamps without wires at a distance of twenty-six miles. Many of the pictures he took showed spectacular patterns of lightning sparks; and in some of the photos, Tesla is seen sitting calmly in the middle of it all (figure 3c). By this time, Tesla was well aware that high-frequency currents had almost no effect on the body, even using millions of volts. The body tissues acted as condensers that were sensitive only to very low frequencies. So there was no inherent danger. Occasionally he witnessed ball-lightning effects - the only artificial ball-lightning ever produced. Physicists still have no agreed rationale for such phenomena.

Possibly his most remarkable finding was the existence of stationary waves which involved the whole earth as a conductor. His estimate of the main resonant frequencies were close to those discovered in the 1960s, and now known as the Schumann waves. In today's world, we envisage the earth being surrounded by various radiation belts that protect us from the sun's harmful radiation, and Schumann frequencies are the natural resonances between the earth's surface and the ionosphere about a hundred miles up. As the earth is bombarded by the sun, our environment 'silently' booms away with these very deep bass notes. The first resonance of about 7.8 Hz is approximately what you get by dividing the the speed of light by the earth's circumference.

In a very long article in 1900 to the *Century Illustrated Magazine* summarising his Colorado findings, Tesla explains in simple language stationary-wave phenomena.

'That communication without wires to any point of the globe is practicable with such apparatus would need no demonstration, but through a discovery which I made with absolute certitude. Popularly explained, it is exactly this. When we raise the voice and hear an echo in reply, we know that the sound of the voice must have reached a distant wall, or boundary, and must have been reflected from the same. Exactly as the sound, so an electrical wave is reflected, and the same evidence which is afforded by an echo is offered by an electrical phenomenon known

as a "stationary" wave - that is, a wave with fixed nodal and ventral regions. Instead of sending sound vibrations toward a distant wall, I have sent electrical vibrations toward the remote boundaries of the earth, and instead of the wall the earth has replied. In place of an echo I have obtained a stationary electrical wave, a wave reflected from afar.

Stationary waves in the earth mean something more than mere telegraphy without wires to any distance. They will enable us to obtain many important specific results impossible otherwise. For instance, by their use we may produce at will, from a sending-station, an electrical effect in any particular region of the globe; we may determine the relative position or course of a moving object, such as a vessel at sea, the distance traversed by the same, or its speed; or we may send over the earth a wave of electricity at any rate we desire, from the pace of a turtle up to lightning speed.'

On this basis, Tesla conjectured that, with waves enveloping the whole earth, there would be, in addition to the nodal point of his laboratory in the Colorado Desert, a nodal point in the southern hemisphere with similar electrical disturbance. Today, we have some evidence for this in the Australian desert areas where major electrical disturbances are now being observed. It is possible that these arise from the new project in Alaska, based on Tesla's own work, in which the ionosphere is bombarded by radio waves, which in turn generate the extremely low frequency waves enveloping the whole earth. Tesla envisaged one day that electrical power costing almost nothing could be provided for all the countries of the world by such means. He also envisaged possible control of the weather, and an electromagnetic shield for the USA.

The Colorado experiments led on to his most ambitious industrial project: a system of "World Telegraphy" that would deliver quantities of power to the more remote regions of the earth. With $200,000 from J P Morgan, in return for the rights to Tesla's wireless patents, the work began in 1900. But after five years of effort, the project far from complete, and Marconi demonstrating long-distance *data* transmission with simpler equipment, Tesla ran out of money. Tesla appealed to Morgan for more finance; but power transmission without wires was never in Morgan's long-term interests. He and other financiers were doing so well out of existing AC systems. This project was Tesla's greatest disappointment, and led to a significant loss of influence over future developments. Looking back over his predictions, power transmission without wires was the only one not be realised during the twentieth century.

There were many other achievements that in themselves any scientist would be proud of. He was the first to demonstrate a radio-controlled device, using a model boat on the Hudson river. His offices were lighted by fluorescent tubes activated by a high-frequency electrical field, and he took out patents on both on arc and fluorescent lighting. He studied fluid propulsion, and used this knowledge to create bladeless turbines and pumps that became very popular because of their reliability. He developed a series of high-frequency oscillators that he considered would be useful in medicine. And applying high electrical fields to himself, he took some remarkable photographs showing his body surrounded with a vivid white halo of electrical streamers.

He spent much of 1896 and 1897 on Roentgen radiation, or x-rays, writing several papers on the subject for the *Electrical Review*, and quickly developing the experimental side as only he could, given his unequalled expertise in AC systems. He showed, for instance, that one could obtain pictures of internal organs at a distance of a hundred feet or more, and was rather worried that these new radiations would affect his photographic studio on another floor.

For serious students of scientific history, these papers about x-rays provide real insight into his methods of work and lines of reasoning. This new field of investigation was quite different from most of his other work in the sense that it quickly became part of mainstream academic research. Several of the brightest university brains such as Lord Kelvin, J.J.Thompson, Oliver Lodge, and William Crookes were seriously investigating Roentgen's most interesting discovery. It was a phenomenon that might or might not fit into the Maxwell theory of Hertzian waves. There is in fact some evidence that Tesla had discovered these rays first; but not having published anything, he gave Roentgen complete credit.

One very obvious feature of Tesla's involvement was the sheer speed of his work, so much being done just in the year 1896, and enabling him to raise so many new questions. From the beginning, he had serious doubts about a theory based on transverse Hertzian waves, and immense frequencies above those of light. He managed to reflect the rays with certain metals, and produced tables for brass, toolsteel, zinc, aluminium, copper, lead, silver, tin, nickel, lead-glass, mica, and ebonite. But he could find no evidence of refraction - the bending of waves passing from one medium to another. This gave rise to speculation about the possible existence of longitudinal waves in the ether - waves that, like sound, oscillate in the direction of propagation.

The more he experimented, the more he likened the behaviour of these new rays to particle streams. Yet, if particles, they were unlike anything else so far discovered. He surmised about Lord Kelvin's ether vortices, the Eastern *akasa*, and Newton's ideas on particles of light. But all experiment suggested the properties of a projectile emitted with immense force. He preferred the term "primary particle", whatever that was. In this, like others of the time, he was feeling his way forward towards subatomic and quantum ideas. That is, extremely high-frequency phenomena beyond the spectrum of light waves behave, in practice, more like billiard balls than waves.

After the intense experimentation of 1896, he then directed his attention during the following year to the possible medical implications, and quickly developed much safer x-ray equipment. Writing a paper for the *Electrical Review* on the 'hurtful actions of Lenard and Roentgen tubes', he warns of four potentially harmful effects. There is a thermal effect which may produce general injury to the tissues; a purely electrical effect which may damage the skin, and interfere with nerve currents; an electro-chemical effect on charged particles that produce ozone and other gases dangerous to the skin; and there is the purely mechanical action of particles travelling at great speed, and possibly affecting not only the skin, but deeper layers of tissues. In this, he set a standard for all scientists and technologists, incorporating health issues right from the beginning of a new field of research.

With financial backing beginning to fall away, and two major fires in which he lost much of his equipment, the new century, which seemed to promise so much, delivered so little reward. He had to learn the hard lesson that in capitalist America, financiers and lawyers held the power. Their attitude was, and still is, that money can always buy brains. He should have been a billionaire himself through the patents he held in connection with the Westinghouse AC power station. But, to save the company from bankruptcy, he generously tore up his royalty agreement.

During the last decades of his life, having no academic or research position, and little capital, he became known more for his futuristic articles and scientific comments. Quantum theory, as it was subsequently being developed by pure theorists, without any notion of electromagnetic stress in the ether, he had huge reservations about - most of his own achievements being based entirely on such a notion. Gravity was a real force producing real waves, not the space-time abstraction of Einstein's theories. While the nineteenth century idolised Tesla for a while, the twentieth century passed him by.

The concept of the *ether* was absolutely basic to all his work. This concept comes and goes in modern physics. To Victorian scientists, it was a magnificent idea, infinitely preferable to action at a distance. Then with the vain attempt to measure the velocity of the earth relative to the ether, and the subsequent theories of Einstein, it became a point of high dogma that there was no ether. And with no ether, there was no field, just interacting particles. Dirac tried to change course, with the suggestion of an ether of electrons of negative mass, but made few converts. Today we talk about a structured space-time, and gravity as a type of strain in this. This would seem to imply an ether, for anything that has a structure must surely be considered a real entity. String Theory seems to make this very explicit.

The reasons why so many physicists of my generation have poured scorn on the ether concept are complex, and based rather on how they would like things to be rather than on experimental evidence. At a high philosophical level, there is a continuing argument about monism and dualism. In the materialist philosophy, as in dogmatic theology, dualism in any form has been high heresy. The concept of matter and ether is one aspect of this heresy. At another level, and probably more germane, the matter-ether dualism has definite spiritualist associations, and these are total anathema to dogmatic monists, materialists, and a majority of theologians. Even just to show the slightest interest in such phenomena has been quite sufficient for total ostracism. How different things were at the end of the nineteenth century when several of our greatest physicists were engaged in serious studies of telepathy and spiritualism.

Tesla's view of the ether was based purely on scientific and technological considerations. It provided for him the mental picture for electrical processes, and hence was the key to all his invention. In a lecture in 1891 to the American Institute of Electrical Engineers about the use of high-frequency currents for artificial illumination, Tesla discusses the ether concept with great enthusiasm.

'**Nature has stored up in the universe infinite energy. The eternal recipient and transmitter of this infinite energy is the ether. The recognition of the existence of the ether, and of the functions it performs, is one of the most important results of modern scientific research. The mere abandoning of the idea of action at a distance, the assumption of a medium pervading all space and connecting all gross matter, has freed the minds of thinkers of an ever present doubt, and, by opening up a new horizon - new and unforeseen possibilities - has given fresh interest to phenomena with which we are familiar of old. It has been a great step towards the understanding of the forces of nature and their manifold manifestations to our senses. It has been for the enlightened student of physics what the understanding of the mechanisms of the firearm or of the steam engine is for the barbarian. Phenomena**

upon which we used to look as wonders baffling explanation, we now see in a different light. The spark of an induction coil, the glow of an incandescent lamp, the manifestations of the mechanical forces of currents and magnets are no longer beyond our grasp; instead of the incomprehensible, as before, their observation suggests now in our minds a simple mechanism; and although as to its precise nature all is still conjecture, yet we know that the truth cannot be much longer hidden, and instinctively we feel that the understanding is dawning upon us. We still admire these beautiful phenomena, these strange forces, but we are helpless no longer; we can in a certain measure explain them, account for them, and we are hopeful of finally succeeding in unravelling the mystery which surround them.'

He then goes on to discuss electricity and magnetism as strains in the ether, and whether or not the concept of two electricities, as assumed by many at the time, is valid. He argues that, although possibly useful in explaining the action of electricity, there can only be *one* such thing, and, *excess or want of that thing*. Through the discovery of the electron, and very basic ideas of an atom, this is a view we have all come to accept. Electricity is an excess of electrons, or a deficiency.

In spite of his achievements, modern British scientists seem to know little about him. He was obviously well known to top British scientists a century ago, and gave a long and fascinating lecture with demonstrations to the Institute of Electrical Engineers in London in 1892 on high-voltage, high-frequency phenomena. As Cambridge was generally considered to be the centre of all things electromagnetic, particularly the theoretical side, its professors were rather surprised to have their experiments and theories commented on, and occasionally criticised by this outsider who seemed to have vastly more practical knowledge. But Tesla could be fulsome in his praise of others; and in several of his lectures, he went right out of his way to praise the contributions of British scientists, particularly William Crookes and Oliver Lodge.

However, I expect J.J. Thomson was a little taken aback by Tesla's comments on one of his papers about electrical discharges in vacuum tubes, maintaining that Thomson was probably interpreting one of his own experiments wrongly in that he did not take into account electrostatic effects on the rarefied gas. This gentlemanly dispute does reflect a basic difference between Tesla and the rest. He understood Maxwell's theory, but often referred to it, and to the associated straight-line electromagnetic Hertzian waves, as a *simple* system. Tesla from very early on, through the luminous effects of fields and currents on gases, was deeply interested in the conduction of electricity through the air. And this led on naturally to ideas about earth conduction, both at ground level and in the upper rarified atmosphere.

Although Tesla did receive honorary doctorates from a very large number of universities throughout the world, including the Sorbonne, Columbia, Vienna, Prague, and Yale, he may well himself have encouraged a certain lack of recognition of his achievements after the turn of the century. Slowly, as his funding dried up, he withdrew from public demonstrations and lectures, living much of his later life as a recluse in various New York hotels, and never joining a research community. But he was probably content in this, for, with his deeply religious conscience, there was a real fear within him of being regarded as a showman. He definitely did not seek or desire worldly fame, although he came close to it in the 1890s. He never became competitive in an American way, or the Edison way, stoically pursuing all his best ideas regardless of cost.

There is little doubt that his futuristic visions and his idealism about humankind puzzled American society, and amused some of the Anglo-Saxons. So when he wrote articles about the development of robots with an elementary "mind" such as we have today, or the waging of war solely with machines and no human casualties, or the development of an electromagnetic shield, he was not taken seriously by the scientific establishment. But he was so far ahead of others at the end of the nineteenth century - in practical applications and in ideas - that contemporary scientists lost contact with him. But he never lost contact with them, often commenting on significant new ideas and experiments, and suggesting practical ways of utilising the new knowledge.

Apart from the biography mentioned at the beginning, which is sometimes dubiously judgmental, the main source of knowledge for many decades was the kindly book written by his long-time friend, John J O'Neill. In addition to his dazzling achievements, we get some sense of the isolation and loneliness of his latter years. We also appreciate his sadness in that the twentieth century used his knowledge as much for destructive purposes as for creative ones.

We learn from O'Neill something of his personal idiosyncrasies. For instance, often referred to is his ability to *image* new inventions - not just vaguely in the mind, but to create precise and dynamic geometrical forms just in front of the eyes. In the earlier part of his life, we are told that these images really bothered him, blocking out normal visual experience. But later, he seemed to make positive use of them.

Tesla had a plausible theory for these creations. Knowing that the optic pathways crossed over behind the eyeballs at the optic chiasma, Tesla surmised that there might be a circular pathway coming round in front of the eyes, and so creating an image there rather than in the back of the brain. Throughout his life he maintained that all his inventions were developed and tested this way before committing anything to paper. Certainly his co-workers were intrigued by the way he could give them very precise dimensions of all the parts to be constructed, and it was assumed that this ability came from his unusual visualisation technique.

I am not aware of any recorded writings on the subject. But in a lecture about light and high-frequency phenomena to the Franklin Institute in 1893, we catch, in his rather poetical prose, a glimpse of his deep reverence for all nature's works, particularly the eye.

'When we look at the world around us, on Nature, we are impressed with its beauty and grandeur. Each thing we perceive, though it may be vanishingly small, is in itself a world that is, like the whole of the universe, matter and force governed by law - a world, the contemplation of which fills us with feelings of wonder

and irresistibly urges us to ceaseless thought and enquiry. But in all this vast world, of all objects our senses reveal to us, the most marvellous, the most appealing to our imagination, appears no doubt a highly developed organism, a thinking being. If there is anything fitted to make us admire Nature's handiwork, it is certainly this inconceivable structure, which performs its innumerable motions of obedience to external influence. To understand its workings, to get a deeper insight into this, Nature's masterpiece, has ever been for thinkers a fascinating aim; and after many centuries of arduous research, men have arrived at a fair understanding of the functions of its organs and senses. Again, in all the perfect harmony of its parts, of the parts which constitute the material or tangible of our being, of all its organs and senses, the eye is the most wonderful. It is the most precious, the most indispensable of our perceptive and directive organs, it is the great gateway through which all knowledge enters the mind. Of all our organs, it is the one which is in the most intimate relation with that which we call the intellect. So intimate is this relation, that it is often said, the very soul shows itself in the eye.'

He then goes on to tell us about Helmholtz, who discovered that the parts of the eye are luminous, and that he was able to see, in total darkness, the movement of his arm by the light of his own eyes. This he considers to be one of the most remarkable experiments ever. He then suggests that when any sudden idea or image presents itself to the mind, there is a distinct sensation of luminosity in the eye.

'The saying then, that the soul shows itself in the eye, is deeply founded, and we feel that it expresses a great truth. It has a profound meaning for one who, like a poet or artist, only following his inborn instinct or love for Nature, finds delight in aimless thoughts and in the mere contemplation of natural phenomena; but a still more profound meaning for one who, in the spirit of positive scientific investigation, seeks to ascertain the causes

**of the effects. It is principally the natural philosopher, the physi-
cist, for whom the eye is the subject of the most intense admiration.'**

With writings like this, it is difficult for modern scientists to know
what to make of Nikola Tesla. They do of course find similar problems
with Newton's theological, historical, and alchemical writings. In my
opinion, it is impossible to put their lives in any sort of perspective
without an appreciation of the strong religious culture in which they
were brought up, and their own lifelong beliefs. With Tesla's father
being a priest of the Serbian Orthodox Church, and his mother very
devout, it was assumed that Nikola would follow naturally into the
priesthood. But he had misgivings about this. During a time when he
was very ill and not expected to survive, his father promised him a
university education in engineering, and the promise was kept. Not that
Tesla was ever the slightest bit anti-religious: throughout his life, he was
greatly supportive of religious work for the good of the whole society,
and the health of the individual. To him, religious leaders, like the leaders
in art and literature and science, were essential for the evolution of
society and the bringing of peace to the whole world. Of the various
religions, Christianity, in its mission of helping the poor, had the greatest
part to play. This is a very Serbian belief, given their history of resisting
powerful tyrants and intolerant religions, and welcoming powerless
minorities like the gypsies. Ultimately, he hoped there would be one
nation and one religion to which we all belonged.

Tesla carried these ideals to the New World when he arrived there
penniless in the 1880s, and retained them, dedicating his life to the
service of general humanity. Although apparently a forgotten figure when
he died in a lonely hotel room in the dark days of World War II,
hundreds remembered and turned out to mourn him in St John's
Cathedral in New York. Three Nobel prize-winners referred to him as
one of the outstanding intellects of the world. All his papers were
impounded because of possible military implications; but most found
their way back to the Tesla Museum in Belgrade through his nephew

Sava Kosanovich. There the memory of his contributions to human civilisation are carefully preserved, and on which my observations are largely based.

In some personal recollections in *Scientific American* in 1917, he stresses the importance and value of his childhood upbringing. And there is no doubt from this article that the invention of the rotating magnetic field, and the forty patents relating to basic AC technology, remained the dominant and pressing matter of his life. Not just because of the success, but also because of the continual strain of protecting his patent rights from ingenious lawyers and experts representing major commercial interests. By 1917 the rights had expired, and he tells us that he had been released from burdensome obligations. Then, with a childlike simplicity, he recounts the "revelation" of the rotating magnetic field that occurred after reciting some lines from *Faust*.

'As I spoke the last words, plunged in thought and marvelling at the power of the poet, the idea came like a lightning flash. In an instant I saw it all, and I drew with a stick on the sand the diagrams which were illustrated in my fundamental patents.

It is extremely difficult for me to put this experience before the reader in its true light and significance for it is so altogether extraordinary. When an idea presents itself, it is, as a rule, crude and imperfect. Birth, growth, and development are phases normal and natural. It was different with my invention. In the very moment I became conscious of it, I saw it fully developed and perfected.'

What other scientist or technologist, apart from Sir Isaac Newton, has had such a massive impact on human society? Through Newton's work, Britain became the dominant technological nation of the nineteenth century. Through Tesla, the USA took over in the twentieth. Both were superb experimentalists, and able by themselves to quickly put together appropriate equipment. Both had the imagination to conceive simple and direct methods of settling a scientific issue. Neither was held back by prevailing dogmatism, or by academic ridicule. Both were of a religious disposition, and committed to the betterment of society. Both were seriously misunderstood by a twentieth-century culture that reverenced Darwin and Einstein and Freud.

In the preface to Tesla's Colorado Springs Notes, the editor has this to say.

'This diary brings to light all that made Tesla different from all other researchers: his creative spirit which often bewildered, amazed, and infuriated many of his contemporaries and even some well-informed scientists, to whom it seemed that Tesla's ideas belonged to the sphere of illusion rather than to the acknowledged course of science. Tesla thus shared the fate of all exceptionally great and far-sighted explorers.

In fact, when one carefully studies the entire work of Tesla, one can see that his principal aim was very clear: to search for the inexhaustible possibilities of dominating the forces of nature and subordinating them to human purposes, thus increasing immensely the power of man and mankind in order to live more humanely.'

What has resulted from this one mind, standing apart, and impervious to all the passing fashions of the day, has been remarkable. He truly lightened our world.

Chapter Four

Changing the Medical Culture

I hope that in this new century we will be more concerned with health than illness. I hope that the word *patient* will disappear from the doctor's vocabulary. Most of all, I hope that we will move away from drug-dependency. One can never be truly healthy on a drug regime, any more than one can be healthy in the drug culture of young people. Whether the drugs are referred to as medical or psychedelic or recreational, the long-term effects are much the same. They weaken our mentality; they harm our body; we lose our sense of purpose; we become a problem to others.

This is a strong statement; and without some recognition of the importance of certain orthodox medicines, herbal extracts, vitamin and mineral supplements, it is an extreme statement. Certainly in particular countries and climates, specific medicines are vital for specific diseases, and artificial supplements are required to supplement dietary deficiencies. But we shouldn't lose sight of the simple fact that many orthodox medical drugs, and those traded on the street, have a common origin, and naturally have much the same effect. Just as scientific farming is now seriously challenged about its use of chemicals, scientific medicine must come under the same public scrutiny.

The first requisite of physical health is a healthy mind, a positive mental approach to all the problems of life. A depressed mind, a worried mind, will inevitably cause a deterioration of the body over time. Why there is the slightest argument today about psychosomatic effects, I have no idea. A simple statement bringing some good news can transform a person almost instantaneously. A dire prognosis of a medical condition weakens the spirit which weakens the body. We have to prepare the mind through suitable ethical education for all situations, good and bad. Whatever their deficiencies and limitations, those in the alternative and complementary fields of medicine all have one thing in common: they aim to strengthen mental attitudes. They also show respect for personal beliefs.

Orthodox medical science today is in a very different situation from fifty years ago when advanced technical treatments first became available to a majority of people. Then, the doctor had almost absolute power, and it was a very unusual person who challenged anything that was being done. We thought doctors knew what they were doing, and anyway, there was no serious alternative. The early pioneers of the National Health Service in Britain really believed that most of the major health problems would be sorted out in a few years, after which they could then concentrate on a few of the more difficult conditions.

Over the last two or three decades, a neutral observer would have to say that, year by year, there is no evidence of any improvement in health, rather the reverse. Cancer has been reaching epidemic proportions. The massive use of drugs for minor conditions, seriously damaging to our immune systems, leads on inevitably to major organ and system failures. Such failures have encouraged the development of new invasive surgical procedures, and ones that involved yet stronger drugs for the suppression of our natural defences, and to be taken for life. This is how we reached the age of transplantation.

Today, many seek out alternatives, believing they have a better chance of remaining healthy outside the official medical systems. Moreover, some in the medical profession who know the real situation, do precisely the same. They are caught up in a system that, on the one hand provides for all the comforts of life, and on the other, could be detrimental to the health of their children. They do have real expertise, and can put it to good use when it comes to physical accidents and standard ailments. But in the meantime, they continue to dish out the magic bullets by the billion, while their colleagues in research continue to promise ever better ones that will release us from all our medical problems.

Over the last decade, there has been considerable optimism in certain medical circles about a new way forward through genetic manipulation. Although there has been almost no practical progress, and some experiments have had serious consequences, there is a view that, with all the new information about gene sequences, the more difficult conditions are ultimately curable by genetic modification. Certainly there are a few specific conditions such as cystic fibrosis attributable to a faulty gene, which then generates a faulty protein. However, even where a single genetic defect is defined and understood, what does one do about the trillions of copies of this gene in the trillions of cells throughout the body? Attempts so far to replace the offending gene using virus carriers have not proved successful.

We are told that many other conditions, including all the varieties of cancer, are supposedly caused or aggravated by groups of genes acting in complex ways. Partly for this reason, billions of dollars have been spent decoding the human genome containing the three billion bases of DNA. Along this base sequence are approximately thirty-thousand genes, each one of which creates a specific protein. Thus, so the theory goes, once we have sorted out the functions of all the genes, we will have the necessary knowledge for sorting out our own structure, our normal functioning, and everything that goes wrong.

Basic evidence about the primary causes of illness points to little in the genetic direction. In fact, it is the resilience of our genetic constitution, and its ability to adjust to extreme physical and emotional stress, that keeps us healthy. What we do know is that environmental pollution causes problems, unhealthy mental attitudes cause problems, emotional stress and loss of family and friends cause problems, a bad diet causes problems. We know that most drugs cause problems. And we know that medical and surgical procedures themselves cause problems. Surely we want to work with the natural genetic processes, rather than reorganise or recode or suppress them.

Some scientists now consider that the new genetic research is unlikely to contribute much to medical practice, and this is expressed openly in the scientific journals. In the sense that the human genome is some type of computer program for the whole body, no programmer on earth has ever got anywhere near this level of complexity. The most complex of computer programs are of the order of a few million machine instructions, and which hardly anyone is likely to understand in full. In the human body, each cell has a program a thousand times larger; and each of the trillions of cells operates the program according to its own needs. To try to assess and treat each medical condition on a genetic basis would require teams of superhuman intellects. And this is ignoring the fact that most of the genome is still a total mystery. Only the gene sequences are understood; and the remainder, generally called *junk* DNA, remains largely unintelligible.

If we continue the computer analogy, no one would ever dream of trying to solve everyday problems by changing the semi-conductor circuitry of the machine. In general, we modify the computer at the electronic level of software instructions. Changing a few genes, which changes a few of the protein building-blocks, would be a form of *re-creation* of the body, and this would surely be a foolish thing to attempt. Better to make changes at a higher level of control - at the electrical level. In doing this, we work at a reasonably understandable level, and involving experimental methods that are readily assessed.

While some medical professionals have already written off genetic therapy, others would argue that the genetic approach must be an improvement on the highly invasive surgical techniques that have grown up during the last fifty years. They can point to many revealing disclosures about modern surgical methods. For instance, we now have it on the highest BMA authority that quite a large number of major operations were performed on healthy people who were assumed to be at risk because their organs were lower than they should be. What eventually transpired - almost unbelievable - is that x-ray pictures were being taken of patients in the upright position, rather than lying down. Gravity was the only thing they were suffering from!

Nevertheless, surgery is the bedrock of orthodox medicine, and one can say that the cruder methods of past decades are gradually being replaced by subtler techniques of microsurgery. Much of our modern surgical expertise originated from attempting to correct or mitigate the terrible effects of weapons of war, and latterly from the carnage on our roads. This knowledge is extremely important; and many of us sympathetic to natural medicine would generally wish to be treated by orthodox methods in the case of serious physical injury. However, when such expertise is applied to organic disease where the origin for the condition may well be excessive drug regimes, or emotional stress, we must have reservations. In some cases like breast cancer, complete breasts and other lymphatic material are removed; in other cases affecting kidneys and lung and heart, whole organs are replaced.

These mechanical procedures have raised some extremely difficult and emotional issues, and which have been subject to little public scrutiny. So much has been done without consent; and so often patients are quite unaware of the long-term implications, such as taking inherently dangerous drugs for the rest of life. They may be unaware of the possibility of failure, and having to start all over again. The side-effects of drugs can only be guessed at, each individual person having a specific response. Most importantly, patients without any medical knowledge are easily talked into having things done to them that may be damaging, and quite irreversible.

Society is hugely divided about all this. There are those who have had major surgery, transplants, heart by-passes, and who now seem to lead fairly normal lives. The fact that there are successes encourages doctors to continue along these lines. But there are an increasing number who do not want to place themselves at the mercy of this experimentation performed by people they know nothing about. Why should they be forced to take such risks with their own lives, particularly with highly materialist people who have no natural sympathy for their ethical and spiritual beliefs?

Fortunately, ours is not the class-ridden society of the earlier twentieth century, when the upper-middle-class doctor was automatically obeyed. There is now the beginning of some recognition that people are clients rather than patients, that they have views and ideas on their treatment, and more and more, that they have access to detailed professional knowledge. While fifty years ago, only the upper classes could challenge a doctor's view with impunity, many today not only challenge, but reject some of the basic assumptions of scientific medicine. In fact, they do not even view it as *scientific*, in the sense that one hopes for something rational and open-minded. If an alternative treatment gives one a good feeling, makes general sense, and does no long-term damage, then why resort to some highly technical, dogmatic, invasive, risky, and drug-dependent approach? This is common sense, and good science.

As important is the psychological aspect. The professional knowledge of the life scientist and medicine man is deeply embedded in the materialist philosophy. Their obvious tendency is to pour scorn on any form of natural healing - through the mind, or through physical contact with a healer. Yet we all know, deep down, that our mental and emotional state very much determines our physical health. The gentle medicine that strengthens the immune system, the kindly advice that changes the lifestyle, the humour that lightens the stress, the love that makes life worth living - all these are surely preferable to spare-part surgery.

Transplantation is medicine taken to a mechanical extreme. Its history is a rather murky one, beginning with a most controversial redefinition of death so that organs could be removed before the heart and blood circulation ceases. Definition of death now depends on the cessation of specific cerebral functions, and not on the heart; and for this, tests are made on certain cranial nerves of the brainstem. Those countries like Japan, which never modified the legal definition of death, did not embark on a transplant programme.

The early recipients of transplants were the guinea pigs for this experimentation, and very few survived for any length of time. Some who experienced several rejections had years of total misery at the end of their lives. There was nothing really humane in all this effort; and those who suffered so much could only be bemused by the international kudos that some of these surgeons acquired. Getting the Nobel Prize seemed much more important than thoughtfully serving humanity.

No doubt many more transplants do now succeed, mainly because of the anti-rejection drugs. But few seem to realise, *prior to having the surgery,* the extent of the complex drug regime required for the rest of their lives. Nevertheless, the failure rate is still high; and after each failure, the surgery tends to be more severe. Failed heart surgery may lead to a failed kidney, then to a brain tumour, and so on. How often do we hear from hospital bulletins that *the transplant was a success, but the patient subsequently died from an unrelated infection.*

Two decades ago, I wrote the following letter to *The Lancet.* They of course regretted that they could not print it. Nothing surprising in this, given that a distinguished surgeon at one of our transplant hospitals, a Dr Wainwright Evans, who opposed the new procedures, was publicly criticised and then censored for his views by this journal.

Now that problems about brain-death have been clarified, and to some extent resolved, I hope we can return to the main issue about the desirability or otherwise of transplant surgery.

Is it worth the cost and effort when so few can be treated, and the results so unpredictable? To what extent are transplants 'necessary', because of previous drug therapies? What proportion of consultants would agree to a heart transplant for themselves? Could it be honestly claimed that a majority of transplant patients have had their quality of life improved? Should we take notice of those who, assuming psychical survival, maintain that removal of organs adversely affects the transitional process?

The questions raised by this surgery go beyond the limited perspectives of medical science. It may be an exciting area of work for the surgeon, and provide interesting knowledge for the academic. But for some of those persuaded into such operations, the results can be extremely sad and tragic. Most of us are quite happy to accept a certain natural life-span, and would wish to avoid any painful and precarious extension involving a high dependence on others. Before we commit ourselves any deeper to transplant programmes, we should surely discuss the issues publicly as has been done with brain-death, and consider the alternatives.

The dubious and sometimes ghoulish experimentation of recent years has produced a significant public reaction against technological medicine. Many are turning towards more natural and much gentler methods; and in so doing, they are being encouraged to take personal responsibility for their own well-being, and to avoid drug dependence. This may be disturbing to the consultants; but in our relatively free society, they still have to prove their case, and convince us that they are proceeding in a sensible, humane way, fully respecting the individuality of every person, especially in the final experiences of life.

People are now opting out of this medical engineering in huge numbers. A friend of mine who has had cancer for several years tells me that, provided he can keep away from doctors (not too easy to do), he thinks he will survive for a few more years. He experiments with various alternative therapies; and even if they are doing nothing very positive, they are not harming him. In particular, his immune system is not being degraded by modern scientific drugs. How is it that doctors, who know better than anyone the importance of the immune system, deliberately encourage treatments that suppress and damage it?

Since writing this letter, I have been more concerned with the situation of the dying donor. Death may be an everyday experience for surgeons; but it is not for each individual person. Apart from birth, it is the most special, the most sacred time of anyone's life. It is a time of the deepest reflection about life's long and difficult journey. How wrong, how cruel it is to invade this privacy with all the technology of the operating theatre.

Transplantation is a striking symptom of a philosophy that has led medicine into strange and undesirable practices, such as routinely removing organs from dying children. We must insist that the human person is so much more than a lump of meat, or a collection of genes. It is thoughts and memories that ultimately define us. Where all this takes place, or at what level of matter or field or vibration, science can only vaguely conjecture. Medicine must show respect for all those who are close to death, and for the view that there is so much evidence to suggest that it is the beginning of some other form of existence. Such respect would transform medical procedures.

A far greater medical problem today is cancer, affecting millions in the Western world. Research into abnormal, cancerous growth is a vast international industry, and for many of those involved, it has become a way of life, allowing for all sorts of specialist studies of the cell and its genes. Possible causative agents like retroviruses have been intensively studied for many years. Yet, as admitted by surgeons, the basic approach to treatment – radiation, chemotherapy, surgery – has changed relatively little in fifty years. There are a few signs of new thinking, such as inhibiting the blood supply to a tumour, but a major breakthrough still seems far away.

The failure of biochemists and physiologists to come up with some fundamental new understanding must prompt the more philosophically-minded to question whether they are working on the right lines. We have had a century of basic embryology, decades of trying to unravel the genetic program of the fruitfly, ten years on the human genome, and yet, as already discussed, our knowledge of growth and form remains just at the descriptive level. If cell chemistry cannot tell us why individual cells develop specialised functions, and cannot provide causal knowledge of the way they aggregate into tissues and organs and major systems, it is hardly likely to solve the problems of abnormal growth.

In *Mind, Body and Electromagnetism*, there is one paragraph on the cancer problem.

Cancer cells are those that fail to work in an integrated way. They appear to assume a life of their own, without reference to their communal functions. After the almost complete failure during the last decade of the most massive research programme in history into these problems, there should now be more interest in those working on a biofield basis. Theorising in these terms, we can envisage that certain cerebro-spinal centres become underactive, or simply fail to function. As a consequence, the biofields are lacking vital frequencies necessary for correct cellular replication. On this basis, the essence of any effective form of cancer therapy involves the correction of the overall field matrix, and this might be achieved through suitable balancing or activation of appropriate centres.

Present orthodoxy is very hesitant about recognising any biofield thesis. Most biochemists seem satisfied with the concept of genes getting switched on or off according to the particular stage of growth reached. As the function of DNA is protein production, the problem of normal growth is reduced to one of generating the right proteins at the right place at the right time. For the embryonic stages, there is speculation about the existence of "master genes" that, from the inner nucleus, determine the external movements and migrations of the embryonic cells.

To those of us in biophysics, it is difficult to be enthusiastic about this line of argument. It is difficult to believe that all this complex chemical activity in individual cells could consistently form the same coherent whole, each with the same intricate blood and nerve and muscle and bone systems that perfectly respond to the Earth's environment. There surely has to be some controlling mechanism, some environmental force-field, some energy pattern that organises the movements and positions and functions of particular cells.

The more one looks at the details of embryological development, the more obvious this looks. Take for example the limbs which develop at very particular positions along the spinal column. How persistent certain spinal nerves are in seeking out their correct limb connections. How remarkable (or natural) that, with a limb cut off, and foreign cells inserted in the stump, a normal limb will grow in some vertebrates. One can do very drastic things, and obviously alter the whole biochemistry, and yet the same pattern of cells and structures will be generated. There is so much to suggest that *a pattern is always there*, and continually encouraging the cells to conform to the pattern.

Prior to the present DNA era, embryologists were slowly feeling their way forward to such a conclusion. During the basic folding process of gastrulation which establishes the three distinctive layers of cells, they had been able to map out consistent patterns of chemical activity, with definite energy gradients from head to tail, and from dorsal to ventral sides. Joseph Needham speculated that, just as electromagnetic field theory had transformed physics, so some analogous field concept would transform biology.

What they did establish in the 1930s and 1940s beyond all reasonable doubt was that development was controlled from the middle layer of cells, the *mesoderm*, these guiding the inner and outer layers into the basic vertebrate form. Add another mesodermal layer from another organism at the same gastrulation stage, and a second axis with separate organs could be formed. Transplant just the head end, or the tail end, and one can get two heads together, or a head at each end, or two tails, or a head that develops like a trunk. Remove the middle layer, and the organism does not develop.

With this conception of a central axis controlling overall development, one is led on naturally to the concept of a biofield emanating radially from the axis. In chapter two, I outlined an electromagnetic approach to the problem on the basis that the middle layer could be thought of as a series of oscillating electrical dipoles radiating electromagnetic fields. Each dipole, with its own specific frequency, will contribute a longitudinal electrical field and a transverse magnetic one; and these two together will create an oscillatory radial pressure according to the basic laws of electromagnetism.

The patterns that came out of this modelling, as shown in figure 2c, were certainly of vertebrate form, with clearly defined head, trunk, and pelvic regions. For a given conduction speed, there was a clearly defined overall pattern, but continuously changing at detailed levels. For a model with small dimensions, the patterns were basically circular like the blastula stage of the embryo, but with suggestions of developments to come. As the size increased, distinctive forms within the three main segments became apparent.

On this basis, abnormal development implies either biofield distortion, or damaged cells unable to respond to the field, or both. In the mathematical model, the obvious way of distorting the patterns is to vary the spinal conduction speed. The higher the conduction speed, the more homogeneous the patterns become, converging towards a simple oval shape like a fish. By contrast, when the conduction speed is reduced, the patterns expand outwards in an increasingly chaotic way. Abnormal growth may therefore imply a slowing down, a lowering of spinal energy flow – and few would disagree with this in relation to cancer.

This in fact is a general, overall view of cancer held by many orthodox and alternative practitioners. Some sort of inner sluggishness sets in, expressing itself physically and emotionally. Through the work of Dr Ian Pierce and others in the 1980s, we came to realise the existence of certain psychological profiles associated with cancer. It is the more introspective or reserved person, not the outgoing extrovert, that that will tend towards cancerous conditions. Negative feelings build up, and are not resolved. This weakens the nervous system, or diverts it from its basic functions, and cancerous cells proliferate unchecked at specific sites. The very mention of the word "cancer" encourages a depressive cycle which can be fatal. Those who let everything out are more likely to have strokes than cancer.

Apart from any psychological aspect, there also seems to be general agreement about other major factors tending to cause abnormal cancerous growth such as bad diet, smoking, and industrial chemicals. Very high frequency radiation (ultra-violet light, x-rays, gamma-rays) is a proven source of cancer, and most of the world now accepts that very low frequency radiation from power sources is also a problem. However, there are clearly health and genetic factors that make some people more resilient than others. Exposure to sunlight, or to nuclear testing, clearly has different effects on different people.

There is no great conceptual problem in understanding any of this in terms of the intrinsic low-frequency electromagnetic biofield of the body. High-frequency radiation, for instance, is not directly damaging to the biofield, but definitely damaging to the molecular and genetic bonding within the cell. The cell cannot then respond correctly to the biofield environment, and cannot perform its communal functions either in terms of protein production or replication. The use of toxic chemicals is most likely to damage the outer cell membranes, and which cannot then respond to weak low-frequency fields. All such damaged cells become foreign bodies.

Mental and emotional stress can be related to low-frequency waveforms, for, through EEG, magnetic resonance, and magnetometer measurement, we can recognise abnormal electromagnetic patterns in disturbed people. These are likely to affect the major nerve and hormone centres, and so disturb natural body rhythms. Sometimes vital activity is lowered, sometimes increased, according to the general disposition of the person and the type of physical symptoms experienced. Where it is lowered, there would seem to be the greater danger of cancerous effects. Alternatively, using mental forces constructively, and deliberately focusing on problem areas, people can develop some conscious control over their internal processes, and improve their general health.

The very low frequency fields from artificial sources are currently a focus of scientific interest. Major American, Russian, and Swedish studies suggest a definite link between the main sources of electricity at 50/60 Hz, and cancer. The principal danger would seem to come from power lines, electrical substations, and the wiring configuration in buildings. At the moment, biophysicists think of these fields, not so much as a direct cause of cancer, but rather that, if cancer cells already exist, such fields may cause greater proliferation by disturbing the bonding between normal cells. This would be completely consistent with the electromagnetic thesis of organic development.

There has been a strange reluctance in Britain to admit to any such link, together with persistent statements from life scientists and government advisors that there was no scientific rationalisation for any such link. The simple fact that electromagnetic fields of very low frequency affect the very low frequency currents of the nervous system, according to the basic electromagnetic law of induction, is conveniently ignored. However, at the time of writing, we have just had the first official admission that there appears to be a link, albeit small, between power lines and leukemia. The rationalisation suggested is that the power lines create positive ions in the atmosphere, and these are generally bad for health. The obvious explanation of induced currents upsetting the nervous system will no doubt be resisted for some time.

Having experimented on myself for many years with low-frequency vibrations, I am convinced that the *method* of applying this energy is quite crucial. Electromagnetic fields from simple coils, for example, can have unpleasant consequences. This is not surprising, for without very specific knowledge of how and where the fields should be directed, and at what frequencies, they are likely to disturb the natural processes within the body. Both the experiments with chicken embryos, and the power line studies, clearly support such a view.

Applying low-frequency currents to the skin would seem to avoid many problems. They will follow the naturally conductive paths of the body, and one can arrange for frequency to vary with conductivity. If applied to the sensitive regions of the hands and feet and ears, or to the acupoints, the energy will penetrate through to the muscles, the spinal cord, and thence to the internal organs. If applied to the whole body, there is a significant increase in conductivity over a few minutes, causing me to wonder whether this is an effective way to energise the spine and its biofield. Having tried this procedure on myself hundreds of times, I have no evidence of any harmful effect. Also, as previously pointed out, frequencies around the note C may help to stimulate the immune system.

Whether or not we can reverse a cancerous condition that may have taken many years to develop by simple electrical methods, current evidence is largely anecdotal. Dr Nordenström of the Karolinska Institute in Sweden did as well as anyone, successfully treating many cases of breast cancer considered hopeless. His therapy was based on observations of unusual electrical potentials building up at the centre of wounds and tumours, and which confirmed some of the findings of Harold Burr. With one terminal at the centre of a tumour, and the other connected to peripheral points around the tumour, he applied pulsed, uni-directional currents for about thirty minutes to reverse the electrical potential. In a good percentage of cases, this was sufficient to reverse the cancerous process, and to allow the body to complete the healing process.

Those of us experimenting in this area do not of course have the luxury of performing orthodox medical trials costing millions of pounds. This is not an option for pioneering outsiders. Moreover, we are not permitted to have the thousands of failures allowed to orthodox doctors. In fact, just one failure for the outsider may result in very serious consequences.

But we must persist. In the same way that certain people can release significant quantities of electrical energy through the hands, and sometimes cure, so it should be possible to do something analogous with technological oscillators. In the year 1900, electrical treatments, mainly direct current, were becoming very popular in the USA, and thousands of doctors were using them. And when Nikola Tesla produced a tunable oscillator for such purposes, it began to look as though medicine would follow this path. Unfortunately, biologists strongly opposed this approach, and eventually the medical establishment decided to follow the orthodox scientific path.

What has been surprising to me about my own oscillator is the effect of just a few milliamps at a few volts. When starting out on this exercise, I simply did not believe that such current levels would have the slightest effect. Nor did I believe that magnetic fields produced by these currents would have any effect. But I was wrong; and many who have tried this oscillator have in fact complained that average current settings, although extremely low, are far too strong for them.

Now I realise it is so much a matter of frequency; and now I believe that if the spine were regularly treated with a natural range of frequencies, then it is possible that an underactive or blocked section of the spinal system could be re-energised, and the whole organism brought into balance again. Even for healthy people, such treatment might induce greater resilience. Beyond this, I look to treatment of specific diseases with specific frequencies, or specific frequency patterns.

Low-frequency oscillators like the TENS (Transcutaneous Electrical Nerve Stimulator) instrument have already had considerable success with muscle conditions, back pain, wound healing and childbirth. There is also a TMS (Transcranial Magnetic Stimulator) that induces nerve activity into selected parts of the brain. The time now seems ripe for some major new experimentation and research with the most serious cancerous and degenerative conditions. This implies a different sort of medical education, and one where physics and mathematics have an increasingly important part to play.

At the time of going to print, I am encouraged to read that a group of surgeons are about to experiment with serious spinal cord injuries where major nerves have been completely severed. Electrodes will be placed above and below the damaged site, and an electrical field applied to stimulate re-growth. Experiments have already been done on animals, with encouraging results. The success of this procedure may well depend on frequency and pulse shape, and about which we have as yet too little knowledge. Thus I expect we need considerable patience for significant results. But in the light of all our new electrical knowledge of the body, it is a most sensible procedure to try.

To try to sum up, we really have to decide what is the sensible *level* to use for medical intervention. Surgery is a crude level, but sometimes necessary; drugs are often too specific, and generally create worse problems in the longer term; genetic modification, if ever found possible, probably leads to infinite complexities beyond the mind of man. My hope is that medical science will, by consideration of relatively simple electrical models of the body, and some basic concepts of electrical resonance in the nervous system, be able to develop new rational and non-invasive procedures. For those who have cancer, I think we have now reached a point in our theorising, and in the development of electronic technology, where this looks possible. Such an endeavour is a major test and challenge for this new century.

Quite naturally, the emphasis today should be on preventive

measures, part of which will be looking after the environment, and part will be looking after ourselves in common-sense ways. The new accent on diet, on meditation, on removing guilt, and generally opening-up people's attitudes, represents positive moves in this direction. It also involves respect for the natural defences and energies of the body, and respect for the beliefs and feelings of each individual soul.

Chapter Five

The Quest for Freedom

Most of us are searching for, reaching for, some aspect of freedom, and nowhere more so than in the political field where the concept is in continual use. For the businessman and those on the Right, the freedom to make as much money as one wants, and use it as one wants, is fairly basic. Money is the means to some sort of personal freedom. Taken to an extreme, with liberty to do almost anything one thinks of, regardless of the wider consequences, this interpretation of freedom tends to negate itself. Legal and social pressures come into play that may take away all freedom.

On the other side of the political spectrum, socialists have more limited objectives, being largely preoccupied with "freedom from" things, such as unemployment, poverty, starvation, and many other matters that the more privileged can take for granted. In order to achieve these objectives, they must necessarily curtail the extensive freedoms of the few for the benefit of the majority. This is the first necessary step towards true freedom.

Another way of expressing this is that one group of people want a freedom for personal enterprise to the point where the concept of society becomes irrelevant. And another group are seeking a freedom for personal development through strengthening society with constraints that make it fairer for all. The terms Right and Left have in the past roughly defined these attitudes, but the distinctions are rather blurred in modern politics. Whatever, our attitude or philosophy about freedom will ultimately determine our views about social justice.

Right-wing politics dominate today, with suitable appeals to Adam

Smith or Darwin. Darwin provides something instinctive, atavistic; Adam Smith is more thoughtful. Writing in a different age and culture untouched by Darwinian thought, he argued in *The Wealth of Nations* that a greedy person could become a public benefactor. Although selfish, he gets things moving, provides employment, and increases capital value. No doubt all societies need that sort of drive and talent. But whether making money through gambling and speculation has any worth is questionable. There are an increasing number of people only involved with paper and machine manipulation, quite independently of the needs of companies and institutions, and these have come to the fore in the commercial life of Western society. In today's global market-place, using the latest software and statistical techniques, so many of our brightest young people are involved in a gigantic zero-sum game that does little for the growth of enterprise or the betterment of society. Their selfishness has few redeeming features.

The Social Darwinians made their influence felt throughout the twentieth century, and, unlike many scientists who tend to be Darwinian in their professional life and socialist in their private life, they do at least have a consistent view. To them, the aggressive pursuit of money is the natural order, corresponding, we are told, with something deeply inherent in man's nature. Animals compete to survive; and we, being just superior vertebrates, have similar competitive instincts which should not be repressed. Competition strengthens the will and weeds out the feeble.

This political fashion surfaced strongly in the 1980s at a time when Darwinism was being seriously challenged in the scientific field as a way of explaining the evolution of organic life. To be a little more accurate, it was neo-Darwinism that was under attack. "Survival of the fittest" has been suitably diluted down during recent decades that it is hardly a significant idea to the specialist researcher. Animals are not struggling and competing in any human sense; rather it is those who accidentally have the most suitable genes that tend to survive better than those with inferior genes. Very simply, some genes are better than others.

Social Darwinians make much of the idea that they are working with the natural grain, rather than against it. Presumably all civilising, cultural and ethical influences are against the grain. But looking at the animal world, it is not clear to me what the natural state is. Most higher vertebrates live in reasonable harmony, and only a few species are unduly aggressive. Most are content to live a communal or solitary existence without harm to comparable animals.

After experiencing the worst excesses of Social Darwinism through two terrible wars, and with unspeakable brutality on both sides, there was nothing much for European politicians to argue about after World War II. We simply had to change our ways. Pursuing the Darwinian road for the first half of the twentieth century, the human race had become ever more violent, ever more scheming, ever more ruthless. In terms of material devastation, and the countless millions slaughtered, the twentieth century was quite the most barbaric of all time. We reached the point where we could, and actually did, wipe out cities in a few seconds. Never would we ever be able to lecture other peoples and races about civilised values.

There was every incentive after the war to bring the financial systems under tight control by governments and international agencies; and for over twenty-five years, currencies were stabilised through the Bretton Woods agreement. Keynesian ideas played a major part in sustaining a controlled growth, and in largely eliminating unemployment and extreme poverty. While there was no consensus to eliminate capitalism, there was a consensus to avoid the Darwinian extremes, and to make the financial systems responsive to the needs of society as a whole. Many services, including the massive provisions for health and education, became available to all without the exchange of money.

In recent years, the Social Darwinians have at least helped to clarify many things. They have made it clear again that money can, without suitable constraints, considerably reduce human freedom for those in the lower half of the economic scale. When the old and handicapped are made to pay for elementary services, money becomes a disturbing form of oppression. Even if people can pay their bills, the chances are that they have to toe the line pretty carefully. Free speech in the workplace is a luxury few can afford. Throughout capitalist society, the continual threat of the withdrawal of the wage or the loan precludes much possibility of freedom. To the early socialists like George Bernard Shaw, a society based on money would always be corrupt; and the long-term aim of socialist movements was for its gradual elimination.

Obviously, our attitude to money, and the way we use it, is a major social issue. The first and most important thing to realise is that we, as individuals, do not own it. That is to say that the value of any coin or note is completely dependent on the whole society in which we live. One often hears people saying, 'It's my money, and I can do what I like with it'. This is not meaningful. Its value at any point depends on the efforts of the whole community, rich and poor, over generations. And those who have demanded the least like teachers and nurses have probably contributed most to the current value.

Apart from the greater convenience over any bartering system, money has two basic purposes for our society. It is a form of rationing, and the standard means of accounting. Whatever way society is organised, accounting in some form or another is indispensable. For most products, the world's resources are finite, and continuous information on supply and demand is necessary for regulation. In fact, the accounting is part of the rationing process. If electricity or gas is in short supply, the crude solution is to make sure that the majority could not possibly have the resources to pay for large quantities. The much more difficult, but fairer solution, is to ensure that resources are evenly allocated, independent of class and wealth.

In the global market of modern capitalism, money is the only form of rationing. Given such a system, it is important that money should be used intelligently, and not stagnate. Every time we get a job done - something designed, something built, something repaired - there is an increase in monetary value. Using money in an obviously productive way is beneficial to all parties, and the real wealth of society increases. It is the overall circulation, by one means or another, that gives life to the economy. If money cycles at a fast rate, the economy expands. If it slows down, perhaps because people are encouraged to leave money on deposit and just collect the interest, then the economy contracts.

This is expressed in economic theory in a rough and ready way by the simple formula $G = M \times V$, where G is the Gross National Product, M is the quantity of money in circulation, and V is the velocity of circulation. In practical terms, V defines the number of times on average that money changes hands in any one year. The usefulness of this MV formula is that it provides a way of discussing some fundamental issues, and suggests guidelines for running the system. Money has a certain *momentum*, using the term in a Newtonian sense. The quantity and flow must be nicely regulated to produce the most beneficial effects. Too much and too strong, and things get out of control; too little and too weak, and the system slowly dies.

To the monetarist, V is relatively unimportant, this supposedly remaining fairly constant whatever people and governments do. Therefore one tries to concentrate on limiting the growth of M so that money generally holds its value, expanding slowly in line with the growth in the economy. In Britain and the USA, the monetarists had their great experiment in the early 1980s. The almost immediate effects were high unemployment, high and fluctuating interest rates, and the destruction of large areas of manufacturing industry. After two or three years, there was overt abandonment of the experiment in the USA, and tacit abandonment in Britain to avoid political embarrassment.

To the Keynesian, V is the vital factor. People need the sort of wages and salaries so that money will circulate as quickly as possible. They must be encouraged to buy, and so keep industry at full stretch. Money has to be used, and made to do more and more until the economy comes into balance with everyone usefully employed. When, through high interest rates, people just sit on their money, the whole process will slow down, and many will be that much poorer. In turn, this will encourage governments to waste these resources on unproductive prestige or military projects.

There are of course many redundant transfers of money between government bodies and individuals, and between central and local authority, that have no obvious productive value. They may represent a certain potential for growth because money is being redistributed. But they are much more likely to be damaging, in that the taxes on the poor are helping to support a wasteful bureaucracy. It is difficult to believe that value-added taxes between businesses, handing over the money to government, and then claiming it back, has any constructive value. Such a circulation of *dead money* certainly discourages the creation of new enterprises.

Today, in surprising and unforeseen ways, *we seem to be moving towards the elimination of money*. It is not happening because of any socialist idealism, but simply through technology. We are certainly reaching a stage when we can question the necessity of having any physical money at all. In the City, money in any old sense has disappeared from the scene. In the big takeovers, nothing as common as coins and notes is ever likely to change hands. In place of these, there are numbers, or binary bits, manipulated by complex software systems that provide for any level of sophistication. Huge loans and payments can be effected at the touch of a button. With the extensive use of credit cards, only a computer accounting unit would seem to be required. And with the credit cards come automatic loans of thousands of pounds, and which now play a major part in keeping the whole economy moving. How difficult it once was to extract such sums from bank managers.

The new computerised systems, working to millionths of a second, have provided a possible mechanism for change. Some advantages are already obvious. Just by manipulating numbers in a computer rather than exchanging cheques and cash, purchasing is considerably simplified, and the number of redundant transfers is being reduced. Benefits for the old and disabled can be automatically made, avoiding all the inconvenience of queueing at the post office and government offices.

More importantly for most people, it should be possible now to consider the elimination of double taxation through the sensible use of electronic systems. We pay one lot of taxes to local government, and we pay another lot to central government. All this involves complex but pointless transfers of money, and a massive civil service to sustain the operation. Through our taxes to central government, large grants are made to local government to help run their services, particularly in education and health. It is difficult to see that such a circulation of money, with an unaccountable bureaucracy, and unnecessary power for national politicians, has any merit for the economy generally.

It would surely help in the furtherance of democracy, and the reduction of centralised political power, to pay just one tax to local authorities, leaving the allocation of funds between local and central government to be sorted out on some percentage basis. Development would evolve on a regional basis, thus adding to the character and variety of the whole country. Using the local taxation systems, it should be simpler to implement an automatic minimum income for every person, allowing sufficient food, clothes, and accommodation at basic levels. Central government would be of a regulatory and advisory nature.

Is this all so fundamentally different - or just the old thing under a new guise? Will it help those that sleep rough, or suffer from hypothermia? Will it allow for the fairer allocation of resources, and the devolution of power? Electronics provides a method for change in our society, without strong centralised control. It provides the potential for many of those desirable things that good people dream of. Through automatic income and taxation systems, resources can be fairly and intelligently distributed without any violent upheaval.

We have the means of change. But the imagination to do something of this nature, that sense of an innate ability to improve the world, depends ultimately on our deepest personal beliefs. If we can accept that the mind is free to make these decisions, and not hopelessly pre-determined by genes or nerves or instincts or whatever, then all is possible. However, behavioural psychologists, in conjunction with the main disciplines of scientific orthodoxy, have tried during the course of the twentieth century to exorcise any concept of individual freedom. To some, all is supposedly pre-determined at any point of time because of the laws of energy, which admit of no exceptions. Others take the view that these laws may be statistical in nature, and so there is the alternative that the world may be essentially random. Either way, through absolute law, or through random patterns, things are inevitable or without purpose. The brain processes, being part of all this, have then no more freedom than anything else.

Such depressing ideas encourage us to consider the religious alternatives. In the Judaic tradition, Man was first given his freewill distinct from all other creatures. But after abusing it, the disappointed Jehovah decided Man was too primitive for freedom, and needed to be circumscribed with the severest constraints. Christ supposedly brought us some relief from this; but within the churches that sprang up in his name, the idea of freedom has been given little encouragement. It is faithfulness to a creed, and to the institutions, that are all-important if we are to attain the final freedom of eternal life. David Jenkins and a few others begin to preach a different and more welcoming message. But to so many trapped in a religious tradition, discipline and ritual are far more important than any spontaneous living and loving.

To some in the West, Buddhism presents a worthwhile alternative, freeing men's minds to explore all avenues. But in its higher philosophical aspects, one finds discouraging parallels with scientific determinism. There is a certain inevitability about the progression of the soul, with an ultimate aim, not to win freedom of thought and action, but to unite with the primordial energy of the cosmos. Agreed, it is not hedged around with puritanical constraints; but it has something of that colourless, dry, neutral nature of modern reductionism that simplifies the world to interactions of subatomic particles, and feelings of transcendence to oddities in the human nervous system. Its sense of justice is rigid and unswerving, all our karmic debts requiring due payment in due kind. The concept of a sudden release from the chains of the past, such as evangelicals preach, would be silly sentimentality.

Undoubtedly, the Theory of Evolution has posed the greatest challenge to the notion of personal freedom in the last hundred years. In its earlier forms, such as propounded by Lamarck, evolutionary processes were seen as purposeful, living forms developing according to intrinsic needs. Those parts of a living system that were much used developed and grew, while inactive parts tended to atrophy. From such an idea, the concept of a developing freedom, first in the physical sense, and later extending to brain and mental activity, could be envisaged.

However, such common-sense ideas have been undermined by modern genetics, and what is called neo-Darwinism. It is doubtful that Darwin would recognise the *new-synthesis*, based on chance mutations and complex statistical analysis. But the upshot of it all is that life is determined by sequences of DNA chemicals in the nuclear material of the cell, and this is unaffected by the way people live and think. Diversity comes about through sexual combination, through freak changes that have survival value, and perhaps some degree of nurture. To the fundamentalists, most of our actions are genetically conditioned, including supposedly the theories we have about genetic conditioning.

Although opposed to the Darwinian advocates, let me hasten to add that I have some sympathy for Charles Darwin himself. If *The Origin of the Species* had been a little shorter, and not so geared to specialists, we might have got his ideas in a rather better perspective. On page after page - although continually apologising for brevity - Darwin argues that the difference between species and variety, in the classifications of the time, were rather dubious. Thus one could not assume that each species was a unique and separate creation. A unusual variety might, one day, eventually evolve into a separate species.

While Darwin rather tentatively put forward his views, always anxious to stay out of public controversy, and avoid upsetting his wife and family, Ernst Haeckel, the most influential German biologist of the time, was just the opposite, proclaiming to the whole world the incontrovertible truth of the evolutionary thesis. Quite logically, he was totally opposed to Christian ideals of a co-operative world, because this weakened the will to survive. Looking at the history of the twentieth century, it has to be said the Haeckel's view and vision, aggressively supported by the biological establishment, predominated for most of it.

A century later, it would seem that the Human Genome project has begun to modify a little the hard-line stance. For most of the twentieth century, there was really no limit to the magical powers of genetic chemicals and processes. Whatever ability we had, whether to write poetry, to understand mathematics, or design computers, there was apparently some gene, or combination of genes, that would do the job. Now that it is known that we humans differ so little from the higher primates in DNA content, there is a cautious change of tone, with a little more emphasis given to the effects of nurture, and possible degrees of freedom in our personal development.

The biochemical view of human nature is part of a long line of thinking going back at least to Spinoza who tried to analyse human behaviour and emotions in much the same way as geometry is built up from an ordered sequence of propositions and theorems. There is no mind as such, certainly no freedom of the mind, and we quietly overlook the difficult fact that geneticists privately believe that they have come to such conclusions pragmatically and *freely*. In Platonic idealism, and much of Indian philosophy, we have the complete antithesis of this, with mind and consciousness at the heart of everything, and all else being variants or expressions of these.

There are many today who, while accepting the concept of the individual mind, have little sense of the freedom of the mind. Everywhere there are esoteric groups who think the mind is just as conditioned by the cosmic forces and vibrations as the body is conditioned by its genes. We are immersed in this great sea of electromagnetic, gravitational, and thought energy, and any attempt to go against these influences is inherently damaging. From their point of view, the only sensible thing is to study these patterns, and the rules that have been handed down from those in former times who were more consciously aware of them, and then do one's best to live in accordance with them. In this, there is a small degree of freedom, but no chance of fundamentally changing our destiny.

I know there are theosophists and anthroposophists who would go way beyond this, seeing Man as slowly extricating himself from these cosmic influences, and gaining a measure of control over his own destiny. George Bernard Shaw's *Back to Methusalah*, which he regarded as his most important work, explores such a theme, suggesting that the human mind will control not only the emotions, but the whole autonomics of nerves and hormones. In this, one can point to Yoga adepts who seem to have made considerable progress along these lines. Ultimately, it is envisaged that mind will take control of the whole physical system.

With such a varied spectrum of conflicting opinion about mind, and will, and freedom, and bombarded daily by politicians, bishops, physicists, geneticists, psychologists, how difficult it seems to get our bearings. And yet maybe not so difficult. The fact that there are so many diverse viewpoints, so passionately held, must surely mean that there is a degree of freedom somewhere. Note carefully that those viewpoints that deny the concept of mind, or its freedom, are supposedly argued for on a *rational* basis. Presumably, any rational decision comes from a consideration of alternatives, and a selection process. If then the final decision arrived at "in freedom" is against the concept of freedom, this surely is a straightforward case of *reductio ad absurdum*, and the premise must be false. I would suggest that only those views that come to a conclusion in essential conformity with the processes that led to the conclusion can be seriously considered.

The attitude of William James, surely one of the sanest and most open-minded of all philosophers, much appeals to me. Having deeply studied all the modern arguments about determinism and evolution in great depth, and from every scientific angle, he finally decided that his first act of freewill would be to believe in freewill. And from there, he tells us, he never looked back. To him, our morality, our religion, our freewill depend on the effort made, and society draws new life from those courageous enough to make the effort.

'The huge world that girdles us about puts all sorts of questions to us, and tests us in all sorts of ways. Some of the tests we meet by actions that are easy, and some of the questions we answer in articulately formulated words. But the deepest question that is ever asked admits of no reply but the dumb turning of the will and tightening of our heart-strings as we say, "*Yes, I will have it so!*" When a dreadful object is presented, or when life as a whole

turns up its dark abysses to our view, then the worthless ones among us lose their hold on the situation altogether, and either escape from its difficulties by averting their attention, or if they cannot do that, collapse into yielding masses of plaintiveness and fear. The effort required for facing and consenting to such objects is beyond their power to make. But the heroic mind does differently. To it, too, the objects are sinister and dreadful, unwelcome, incompatible with wished-for things. But it can face them if necessary, without for that losing its hold upon the rest of life. The world thus finds in the heroic man its worthy match and mate; and the effort which he is able to put forth to hold himself erect and keep his heart unshaken is the direct measure of his worth and function in the game of human life. He can *stand* this Universe. He must be counted henceforth; he forms a part of human destiny.'

Of course, if we choose not to evolve, not to exercise our freewill, not to see any alternatives, then this will be self-fulfilling. But having decided to the contrary, to use our mental freedom, it will grow according to use – precisely in the Lamarckian way. In a different way, David Jenkins talks about the freedom of Christ, with an unknown future that is there for us to determine. There is thus no inevitability about poverty, unemployment, or nuclear war if we choose to believe otherwise. Everything depends on our decision to use our freedom; and to use it responsibly so that our freedoms grow together, and not just to the advantage of the privileged. Acting in a thoughtful way is part of our freedom. Acting in a callous way is also part of our freedom. But in limiting the freedom of others, we damage the concept, and ourselves, and others.

Most scientists do have a certain respect for Christian ethics, even though sceptical about the theological doctrines that go with it. With Haeckel, it was quite the opposite. It was *The Sermon on the Mount* that was so wrong rather than any institutional ritual. We were part of a pre-determined world, with no freedom of the will, no soul, and only instinctive drives urging us to compete and conquer. His influence on his contemporaries, and subsequent generations of scientists and politicians, was immense. Through his own creation, the German Monist League, he argued for colonisation programmes, racial purity, and other nationalistic measures that were later to be so important to the Nazi movement.

While our modern evolutionists may not have the consistency of Haeckel, they do have his persistence. For Jonathan Miller, one of our greatest exponents, modern Darwinian philosophy is all-embracing, covering the whole panorama of biology, psychology and medicine. Anything not in conformity with a monist, reductionist, Freudian, Darwinian scheme of things becomes a natural target for ridicule. Yet when confronted with man's inhumanity to man, particularly what happened to the Jewish race when subjected to the full force of Haeckel's Social Darwinism, scientists recoil with shock and horror. As can be read in *Nature*, discussion of such matters is not helpful, and is best avoided.

Nevertheless, our Darwinians remain a fierce breed. They took control of the academic biological schools about a century ago, and have hung on very tenaciously against all-comers. Lamarck's sensible evolutionary thesis they unnecessarily made into a major heresy, and effectively stopped all research along those lines. And any traces of vitalism, dualism, and pluralism - including electromagnetic studies - they have poured their collective scorn over.

During the last few decades, they have effectively taken over control of the media, especially television. Almost all nature programmes are presented with a suitable Darwinian bias. Even the liberal David Attenborough makes the appropriate noises to please the academics in his audience. Reading his book *Life on Earth* from an agnostic viewpoint, he gives the impression of an "unconscious creationist", often thrilling us with the wondrous subtleties of nature's ingenious processes.

As with cosmologists, it is rather nice to have a subject that one can be totally speculative about, moving from one exotic concept to another, and never having to worry too much about verification. How easily it trips off the Darwinian tongue that 'six million years ago, such a species came into existence' - although little different in character from those who state as often as possible that the universe was created fourteen thousand million years ago, plus or minus a few billion. One is inclined to have a little sneaking sympathy for the Creationists who object to seeing these "facts" put forward in all school textbooks. If science is ultimately about verification or falsification, and specific things are beyond these, they can never form part of the main body of scientific knowledge.

Alexander Dubrov's new evolutionary thesis, first published in 1978 in his book *The Geomagnetic Field and Life,* and involving specific causal factors, is a very welcome development in evolutionary thinking. The idea that we are unaffected by the planetary forces of the magnetosphere surrounding the earth, and by gravitation, is just too implausible. Our lives are so obviously influenced by the whole cosmic environment, not just by the local chemistry. In this thesis, electromagnetism is the vital life-giving essence, and gravitation the stabiliser. All the rhythmic cycles in our bodies, from hormone levels to brain waves, follow the daily cycle of the earth; and from conception, the genetic patterns and growth processes are influenced by the local geomagnetic field. The reversal of north and south poles, which occurs about every half-million years, seriously affects the magnetic polarisations of molecules and genes, and gives rise to basic species changes.

Overall, Dubrov provides a different emphasis about organic development, with Darwinian chance and probability being replaced by definite ideas of causation. It is a more optimistic view of our situation, and, in my opinion, more plausible. And based on real evidence from thousands of researchers, many would see it as more truly scientific.

Our biologists, who tend to shy away from anything related to electromagnetics, seem unwilling to take up the challenge. But there are chinks of light, with a few beginning to redefine their evolutionary beliefs, and to realise certain broader responsibilities. Scientists, now consulted extensively by government on so many issues, are being forced today to consider the social implications of their theorising. Richard

Dawkins, for instance, while being one of the truest believers in the Darwinian thesis of animal evolution and one of its greatest apologists, now states that the consequences for human society of Darwinism are extremely undesirable. Most scientists that I know today are anxious to see a fairer society, in spite of their reductionist philosophy.

The quest for freedom is something very basic in us; but without the restraining influence of justice, our freedom may not be worth having. Certainly the way society is organised, and our approach to money, is extremely important for creating a free and fair society. The equitable distribution of world resources, the end of greed and exploitation - these are the natural goals towards which people of goodwill should be striving. Sadly the dictatorial communistic experiments set back this process, in spite of the obvious advances made by Scandinavian democracies.

One sometimes looks longingly back to past centuries when whole communities and several generations could be occupied in one significant undertaking, like the building of a cathedral. Even today, in the restoration of these buildings, one cannot help being struck by the sense of purpose that such a long-term project helps to foster. Those countries experimenting with something more communal, and trying to build for the long-term, have immense difficulties with our current obsession about the global market.

Individually, it is what we choose to believe, our personal religion, that determines any sense of freedom. Either we sense within ourselves a freedom to think and act and make a difference, or we do not. Just as the belief in freewill reinforces itself, so non-belief makes us rather helpless. Hopefully, enough of us can reject such pessimism, and recover those values that once fired our post-war reformers striving to create a tolerant society. Eileen Garrett is completely optimistic.

'Mind is the true force that creates all things in the Universe. Just as the architect must image in his own mind the building he will some day erect, so must mind in the Universe conceive all things before they can be born. First comes the image or vision

to the artist or creator and then follows the realisation of that dream in a completed work of art, or a world.

In the not far-distant future people will become more consciously aware of the tremendous power which is contained in thought and how it acts throughout the universe, incessantly charging and recharging the current of our daily lives. For let me repeat and emphasise, thought is an active force, going forth from man's mind like a flash of lightning, which strikes and affects other minds as it moves and travels through space. It is so potent that it can make or mar us. If we realised the inherent and compelling power of thought to direct and control, or create and destroy, we would think deeply and constructively before allowing ourselves to be drawn into much of our useless living. Thought is the great motivating power from which all desire stems. And desire is the breath of the Infinite within all pulsing life.'

Chapter Six

Miracles and Oddities

Having no conception as to why there was ever anything at all, and continually coming back to this central mystery, there is little tendency for me to get excited about unusual events. Some I know witness a little miracle, and their whole belief system changes overnight. But if you take the view that all of life is quite miraculous, then you don't get caught off balance in this way.

Sir Isaac Newton has given us an excellent definition of a miracle.

'For miracles are so called not because they are the works of God but because they happen seldom and for that reason create wonder. If they should happen constantly according to certain laws impressed upon the nature of things, they would no longer be wonders or miracles but might be considered in philosophy as a part of the phenomena of nature notwithstanding that the cause of their causes might be unknown to us.'

There are specific things that fascinate me, things that are out of the ordinary, and that seldom happen. But there are also very ordinary things that fascinate. For instance, in typing this chapter, my conscious mind still does not know after all these years the positions of all the letters on the keyboard - meaning, if you asked me to sit down with a blank sheet of paper, and write down the position of each letter, I could only do it by the most indirect method. I would have to imagine myself typing a word containing a particular letter, and so get an approximate position for it. A further oddity is that, when I come to a difficult word with several similar consonants or vowels, the only way to be sure of typing it accurately is to close off my conscious mind, and then type as quickly as possible. Words like phenomena, or autonomic, come out perfectly when I leave the subconscious to do the work undisturbed. However, in a very few cases, the converse applies, with the subconscious always seeming to reverse two particular letters. I should add that I am an untrained typist, using only two fingers.

Well that is rather mundane stuff to many. But with a Celtic cast of mind, I am continually mystified by what Anglo-Saxon scientists get excited about. With their subservience to prevailing dogma, they tend to make unnecessary problems for themselves.

For example, I am not surprised when I hear of one person healing another through simple contact or massage. The two bodies have similar energy fields, and if anything is going to influence the human body - for better or worse - it is likely to be something of similar energy constitution. I am far more amazed that the body is able to cope with some of the modern surgery, involving the insertion of materials quite foreign to the body, or of organic matter from a different genetic source.

We hear about miracles almost all the time these days, particularly on television, where so many now testify that they have been miraculously cured in a single session with a healer. There is also the miracle of the placebo, or even the simple giving-up of orthodox treatments. Doctors have certain normal expectations about the course of a disease, based mainly on statistical evidence; and when something different happens, and the disease disappears, we have a miracle of sorts.

If we think about Newton's definition, then the more often these things happen, the more we should be trying to absorb this knowledge into some philosophical framework. Just to reiterate over and over again that alternative treatments have no rational basis is not a very intelligent thing to do. On a chemical basis, they may make little sense. But on an electrical basis, they could make eminent sense.

When electrical and electronic equipment malfunction, we naturally assume some one component, or some one connection, is faulty. A single and simple fault easily causes a complete breakdown; and after that is sorted out, normal functioning is resumed. So when I hear that a person is in a really bad way, with high blood pressure, arthritic conditions, weak heart, and confined to a wheelchair, I take the view that all this may be caused by a single blockage in one of the major nerve pathways. Thus, when a healer comes along, intuitively finds the problem area, and gently stimulates that area, it would seem to me quite normal and reasonable that everything may get corrected very quickly. And, on the other side of the coin, it is also normal and reasonable that orthodox pills and operations might tend to make things worse.

Continuing this line of reasoning, it is possible to achieve even more miraculous results if the basic condition is psychological. A few kindly words that change the whole mental focus can re-energise the cerebrospinal system, and quickly bring things back into balance. Alternatively, a lot of different things may be fundamentally wrong, and cannot be all be corrected at the same time. In this case, natural remedies are unlikely to be effective in the short term.

Therefore, on this basis, we may expect miracles from time to time, and we may also expect total failures in many cases. The rational approach to such evidence is to try analyse the effects of a healer, in the hope that we can reproduce them to order. Whatever, it is ignorant to sneer at clear-cut healing evidence just because it doesn't fit the laws of organic chemistry.

There are the same sort of controversies about memory regression through hypnosis, particularly when it goes back centuries. But why? If one assumes the existence of the eternal soul, this is a natural phenomenon. If one is a materialist, these are genetic residues. And if one is somewhere in between, the possibility of the geomagnetic field holding memory material is reasonable enough. Similarly for spiritualist phenomena - there are no great problems of some level of rationalisation, whether in terms of spirits, telepathy, intuition, or deep memory. The childish attempts by many scientists to prove all this is a fake - for fear of disturbing the scientific consensus - is rather pathetic. Fakes are found is every branch of human endeavour, and the scientific community

99

contains more than its fair share, being so pressured by money and fame to produce results.

To get the basics of a subject, one should always try to go straight to the best evidence available, and to the best people. While a huge amount of psychical evidence can so easily be written off, if there is five per cent, or even one per cent, that stands up to all reasonable tests, and is produced by people of high integrity, then we have something worthwhile to investigate. In psychical research, once we become acquainted with people like Eileen Garrett and Edgar Cayce - both having a healthy scepticism about the material they generated - we can begin to take many new things into our experience in our stride.

It is because of their total honesty that these two good people are seldom mentioned by the orthodox debunkers, and so remain little known to the general public. Edgar Cayce produced vast quantities of unusual information about thousands of people over a period of forty years. After being hypnotised for a throat condition in his youth, and eventually being cured, he found he was able to go into a self-induced trance, and provide information about people's past, or their illnesses, or simple factual information about what they were currently doing perhaps hundreds of miles away. Almost every afternoon of his adult life, Cayce's subconscious answered specific questions, and gave specific remedies or advice on a great variety of problems, both personal and abstract. He himself remained doubtful of the material, particularly all the more esoteric aspects seemingly at odds with his Christian beliefs. He could have become very rich, but he never abused his talents in this way, living and dying in simple circumstances.

Eileen Garrett was a much more sophisticated person, becoming a great favourite in London and New York society. So many scientists wanted to explore her psychical powers. Throughout her life, there were "guides" who seemed independent of her own psyche, and provided answers to many perplexing problems, including much technical information on the R101 airship crash, and which was well studied by the Air Force authorities. Eileen had all the psychical talents, but used them sparingly and intelligently, never letting them take over. She did many interesting things in a very full life, including running her own publishing house for ten years in New York.

Here were two worthy people anxious to broaden the horizons of science. Yet so much effort today is expended on proving that some third-rate, publicity-conscious practitioner is a fraud and a charlatan.

An interesting thing about Eileen was that she herself was not convinced of the spiritualist belief of contact with discarnate souls. Every manufactured article, for instance, seemed to her to be impregnated with basic memory records of its history and use, these producing distinctive mental images and impressions. Eventually, she decided that her special abilities should be scientifically explored. So in cooperation with Dr. Rhine, parapsychology came into being at Duke University.

Even more interesting was that she became disillusioned with parapsychology, with its boring card-guessing games totally without emotional content. To her, a guess was a guess, a mindless exercise, and her special talents had little chance to function in these statistical experiments. In her later years, her interests turned largely to natural healing. The following extract is very typical of her persuasive and prophetic writings.

'I have often spoken of radiation as my own means of contacting the world of outer events; especially do I use it as a way of relating myself to that supernormal world of which I am constantly aware. While the process of man's own radiation is as yet so little understood or accepted by Science, I am convinced that in the near future the exploration of the magnetic field will prove that man is a living "world" or "sun", and that he is surrounded by a certain nimbus, as are all light bodies; and it will also be discovered that this field or nimbus which envelops his physical body connects him and his consciousness with the mind of all other forms of life, as well as the greater Mind of the Universe. With the growing knowledge of the science of light and colour, man will be able to photograph the form of the magnetic field which envelops him and every other living organism.

New precision instruments will soon be built to register man's own radiation and its relationship to other types of energy in the Universe. These will have to be more delicate than any yet constructed, in order to catch the swiftly moving emanations radiating from the body, as well as the brain of man. Eventually man will begin to discover that his own body has within and without it the answer to the meaning of his existence on this earth, and to the riddle of all those other states of consciousness which baffle him today.'

To this day, the unfortunate Rhine legacy continues to dominate parapsychology. Were she alive today, I expect Eileen would take the view that it was a mistake to have a separate subject called parapsychology, just as it is probably unwise to have categories of paranormal or supernatural. Her view was that the talents of the few would one day become relatively commonplace. The word *normal*, anyway, is so misleading. What infinite mysteries lie behind the simplest things of life.

If one goes back a hundred years, both the normal and the abnormal were studied together, including the many and varied aspects of the trance state. All psychologists were expected to be practised in the art of hypnosis, for this seemed to be the key that would unlock the secrets of mind and memory. In, for example, William James's classic text, *The Principles of Psychology,* one finds much fascinating information on this aspect, and which has largely been forgotten. Jung was also deeply involved in this in the earlier part of his career. Yet after making a truly miraculous cure of a crippled lady through deep trance in front of his students, he curiously decided not to follow this path further, but to concentrate on conscious awareness of mental and psychosomatic problems.

For most of the twentieth century, there was a curious resistance to the study of hypnosis by both scientists and churchmen. The latter is particularly odd, for the methods of religious ritual combined with soothing music are surely calculated to induce a mild hypnotic state, and in which certain ideas can be reinforced. Materialist scientists on the other hand just don't want to know, for it runs counter to all they wish to believe in. In my opinion, hypnosis is an everyday event, happening to most people sometime during their lives. A few, with a tendency to autism, probably live much of their lives in such a state.

I have never been consciously hypnotised in my life. That is, the few occasions when someone has specifically set out to put me into a trance state have never been successful. Nevertheless, I can say that I have been deeply hypnotised hundreds of times, and against my will. It took me some years to realise what had happened at school when my History teacher, whom I liked and respected, stood in front of a class and proceeded to talk for about half-an-hour on some subject. The voice was calm and soothing, and I really wanted to take in what he had to say. Yet after a few seconds, I was away in some dreamland, and never had any conscious knowledge of what he said. This was always embarrassing: every lesson I vowed to stay awake, but every lesson I failed. It was not until I met some people in the forces experimenting with hypnosis that I began to appreciate what had happened at school.

In all science, it is the unusual, the abnormal, the unexpected, that throws light on the normal. The physical sciences continually progress in this way. One first establishes a certain body of experimental information, and consolidates with relevant theory. Then one day something abnormal occurs, something not covered by the theory. This creates a new line of research, and a challenge to theorists to incorporate both old and new into some more comprehensive formulation.

By having the normal and abnormal separated out, with different specialists for each, the subject of psychology is unable to grow in a natural way. The practical consequence has been that the mainstream academics have become more materialist and behaviourist orientated, while those on the fringes, often with limited orthodox knowledge, have tended to flit from one rather inconsequential thing to another. Between these two, some of the most basic investigations into mind and memory easily get lost. If there are to be plausible theories of mental phenomena, I would suggest that these can only be developed intelligently with all the evidence available, normal and abnormal.

The suspicion is growing that many unusual phenomena might be rationalised in terms of low-frequency effects. The strong and stable field of one person, for instance, may help to balance and strengthen the energy field of another. Those with a surplus of such energy might have the potential to produce other curious phenomena. Magnetic fields have mechanical effects, minutely altering material dimensions. If one can amplify these effects through resonance, and direct them with mental concentration, curious paranormal abilities might be explained in principle.

Along such electromagnetic lines, the various psychological schools could possibly find some common ground, and develop new ways of exploring basic problems of mind and memory. In the process, certain religious claims about miracles may receive a little more credence; yet at the same time, with some of the mystery removed, we may be encouraged to seek out what is intrinsically worthwhile in religious thought rather than settle for a faith dependent on supernatural events.

Most of us though are more fascinated by little oddities, something whose uniqueness can be immediately appreciated. I once knew a doctor with Parkinson's disease, and who, in his normal working life, exhibited the usual symptoms of the condition, with lots of involuntary muscle movements and hesitant speech. Yet the same man was the star of the local dramatic society. Once in another part, there was a complete change of manner and speech; and for the period of the play, he became another personality unaffected by the disease. Later I found that it was not just a matter of *acting* another part, he was also able to read poetry to an audience with confidence and ease. It seemed that only a formal stage setting was necessary for this little medical miracle.

Not long ago there was a man on American TV who remembered the weather for every day of his adult life. Also in the same program was a person with almost every physical deformity, and quite unable to cope with everyday life. Yet when seated on a piano stool, he could play some of the most difficult music in the classical repertoire, and perfectly replicate complex piano music at first hearing. In Britain, we have recently been watching some of the unusual talents of autistic children, including the ability to draw complex scenes with great accuracy and speed, and from any angle or height. People under trance also exhibit high-speed drawing abilities, sometimes in the style of an old master.

For me, unusual musical ability - keyboard virtuosity, reproducing music at first hearing, speed of composition, sight-reading full scores - is always fascinating. And when I try to relate science to performance, physiological theory actually transforms keyboard playing into a miracle. How could the slow nerve currents, squirting out chemicals into the nerve-muscle junctions, possibly account for what pianists do? A few years ago, a well-educated person told me of his experiences watching a certain renowned pianist at a concert. There were, he explained, these two long pulsating tubes of energy coming down from the back of the neck, and enveloping his arms and hands. Now that to me made eminent sense: the idea of an all-embracing energy field that carried the hands with it, and responding immediately to mental intentions. Wilhelm Reich, like Mesmer, thought it was all a matter of magnetic forces and fields.

For many of us, it is the completely unexpected coincidental experiences that shake us out of the cynicism of everyday life, and leave us with really enduring memories. I remember most clearly one particular day many years ago. My mind had been steadily moving towards a certain critical decision affecting all aspects of my working life. Recent events had suddenly brought things to a head. So there I was one evening in a London station, and pondering what I should do next. It was a large spacious platform, almost deserted, a sort of no-man's land. It was not a part of London that I normally frequented. I must have stood there for about five minutes trying to decide the next move. Suddenly there was someone over at the barrier about sixty yards away shouting my name. Why should anyone do that in this part of London? He started waving his arms frantically, and I slowly moved over to see what it was all about. There, amazingly, was an old friend that I hadn't seen for about fifteen years, and who had recognised me

105

from that distance after all those years. We went to a café, had a long chat to catch up on the past; and through it, my immediate problems just seemed to fade away.

After reading the tea-leaves in my cup, a friend once told me that I needed to be particularly careful because there was a picture of someone about to fall down and with hands in the air. A few days later, being taken round an oil refinery then under construction, I placed my foot carefully on a wooden board covering some hole in the ground. Immediately the board split, and I was on my way down. Somehow I managed to get my arms and elbows in the way, and with pressure on the rim of the hole, held myself with head just above the surface until someone at last noticed my plight. Out I came, covered in mud and thoroughly bruised.

I do wonder whether the new technologists have lots of odd experiences, but are too embarrassed to talk about them. Certainly in the lives of many inventors, there has been a definite mystical element - could it be otherwise? The subconscious, or whatever, has curious pictorial methods of suggesting new ideas. Even the most pedantic scientist accepts the story of Kekulé discovering the ring structure of benzene through a vivid dream about a snake eating its tail.

One strange incident remains particularly clear in my mind. Three of us were working on a difficult project that kept us going, testing and re-testing, all hours of the day and night. There was real danger of the project being cancelled because some thought the problems would never be resolved in a reasonable time-scale. We finally got to the point of clearing all the major problems except one, and everything depended on a solution to this. Eventually there was one day left before the client came over to conduct the critical tests. Now prior to going down to London the evening before, my eldest daughter had been doodling on a piece of paper, and which for some inexplicable reason I had picked up and taken with me. On it she had written the letters DSA several times. During the night, we started getting the message "error DSA" on the printer - one that we didn't know existed in the system. This pointed us in the right direction; and after getting this message several times, a solution was found.

Another oddity of this nature was intriguing. All day I had wrestled with a logical problem in a computer program. Over and over I perused the offending section of code, unable to detect any flaw in the logic. Then just as I was giving up for the day, a little insect came onto the page, crawling forwards and backwards along a particular line before disappearing. After a night's sleep, I woke up realising there was a general logical fallacy with that particular line, although not containing any specifically erroneous terms.

When friends and relatives die, many of us experience little oddities, often quite comforting. I was living about fifty miles away from where my mother died. Although she had been ill for some years, there was no indication that she was about to die. That night, for the first time in my life that I could remember, I got up and made a cup of tea in the middle of the night - and about the same time as she died. When a favourite aunt of mine died, a picture that had family connections fell from the wall, although seemingly well supported. It was undamaged.

Such little personal experiences, of no general interest, and outside the great scientific scheme of things, keep our curiosity for life active and vital. And everyday things, like watching our friends develop and mature, and seeing the changes reflected in the face, are perpetually intriguing. *'Nor do I ask of physics how goodness shines in one man's face, and evil betrays itself in another'*, says D'Arcy Thompson, that lone common-sense prophet of twentieth-century science.

When I was young, I used to say to myself that if ever I understood the lines on a person's forehead, then I would really have made progress in understanding the world. What secrets of joy and suffering they hold. Of such are the Celtic mysteries.

Chapter Seven

Human Memory

Over the past few years, much has been written in the scientific journals about a possible *Theory of Consciousness*. Personally, I have no idea what is meant by this. It seems to make no sense whatsoever. So much so that it is difficult even to say why it is such a nonsense. Presumably biologists think of some molecular or genetic or cellular pattern of activity that has the power to analyse itself. But it is only because of consciousness that we can begin to talk about molecules and genes and cells. These scientific entities are constructs of consciousness; they would not exist without consciousness. In fact, nothing in the whole cosmos would exist without consciousness. The idea that the derivatives of consciousness would then provide some explanation of consciousness itself is, to my mind, a meaningless abstraction.

There are of course various *states* of consciousness that relate to physical and electromagnetic processes, and we can make interesting comparisons about the waking state, sleep, and trance. In particular, the different frequencies of the brainwaves - the idling alpha, the waking beta, the sleepy delta, and the abnormal theta - provide the beginnings of some sort of scientific discussion of these states. But no one would try to maintain that the beta-frequency range does anything to explain the waking state of consciousness. Our thought processes are so infinitely complex, and cannot be reduced to simple waves or particles.

Intimately related to all thought is memory. If we are to understand anything about the mental processes, we should surely first concentrate on the nature of memory. We have no idea as yet where it is stored, how it is organised, how it is retrieved, in spite of the fact that electronics experts have over the last few decades created artificial storage and retrieval systems of great power and versatility. So although there is no theory of human memory, we are beginning to appreciate what is involved in the creation of memory, and therefore perhaps better able to develop a useful new vocabulary about it. Therefore while I think any theory of consciousness is a total non-starter, a theory of memory might be worth pursuing.

We have some useful intuitive and practical knowledge of memory, built up through our various cultures. We know that, for most people, memory needs to be deliberately developed - by disciplined learning and hard experience, through focused interests and religious ritual, and generally through acts of individual will. However, certain natural talents such as with music and languages may involve very little effort, and the learning processes seem more a gentle reminder of something already known.

Compared with our electronic systems, human memory is a more dynamic process, memory records seemingly being continuously created, or lost, or reorganised. Certain matters affecting everyday life, such as language, professional skills, deep emotional experiences - these become almost permanent through their constant use, or the constant replay in the mind. Less important things disappear rather easily from conscious reach, although there is much hypnotic evidence to suggest the existence of a subconscious memory containing the essence of all experience. Some things we deliberately file away to the furthest recesses because they may be too damaging and painful.

The recall, or replay of the human memory is a much more elusive matter than with technological systems. While there are those things that we have immediate access to because of continuous use, there are also distant long-term memories that, even with the weakening of the daily memory, remain easy to recall to the end of life. I can remember for instance all the best and the worst of my performances in music and sport, even though I tend to forget where I put something five minutes ago. I remember clearly all the difficult examination papers when things went wrong, and the embarrassing moments in public life. Memories of life in the forces fifty years ago, when we were so physically and mentally challenged, have remained strong and vivid. In fact, any significant emotional event of previous decades can be replayed, even relived, with great accuracy.

Particular facts, especially names, begin to elude us as we get older, and it is often necessary to create special artificial associations to remember them. In my own case, for instance, I used to forget, for quite unknown reasons, the name of Oliver Lodge, even though I often thought about his life and beliefs. But once I had retrieved the name Oliver, the Lodge just seemed to follow. So today I have him firmly associated in my mind with a different Oliver that I once knew and never forget, and I no longer have a problem with this name. This association process, even though seemingly rather absurd, somehow provides a practical method of access to a specific memory record. The concept of a *path* to a memory record is surely a meaningful one. Sometimes we can find the path, sometimes not.

The sheer power of human memory seems to distinguish us from the animal world - both the ability to store information and impressions, and the ability to recall and replay the material. I stress both aspects, because it is quite possible that animals automatically store all impressions from the outside world much as we do, but lack the ability to retrieve this information at the conscious level. Human intelligence is, more than anything, the easy ability to retrieve and compare memory data from diverse past experiences. However, I am sure many animal lovers are completely convinced that their pets never forget anything.

The memory necessary for language certainly sets us apart from all other living creatures. While the most advanced of animals seem only able to retain just a few dozen distinctive sounds, most human beings can cope quite effortlessly with many thousands of words – their sound, their meaning, their spelling, together with all the rules and subtleties of sentence construction. Some talented linguists may be fluent in up to about a dozen languages, perhaps involving a vocabulary of the order of a million words.

Prodigious memory feats in music are always a source of amazement.

To play a piano concerto by heart involves remembering ten to thirty thousand separate notes, their precise order and timing, the necessary fingering and pedalling, the expression of each phrase, and all the important details of the orchestral score. The full repertoire of a pianist may involve a hundred or so works learnt to a similar level, together with a much greater number known to a lesser level. Somehow, somewhere, several million notes are recorded, and are immediately retrievable.

In spite of minimal evidence, neuro-physiologists sometimes publish hopeful phrenological diagrams of the cortex, and ascribe memory a place somewhere around the temporal cortex of the left or dominant hemisphere, and close to the ear. But they know this is highly speculative. While there is distinctive evidence that long-term memories can be activated with a vibrational probe around this general area, there is no basis that the memories reside in this part. Removing the cortical material does not seem to remove the memories.

There is some evidence to link the hippocampus at the top of the brainstem with the establishment and replay of memory, for damage to this part of the brain can produce memory failure. But the evidence would suggest that this is a failure of conscious access to memory, rather than an elimination of the memory records themselves.

Nevertheless, the search goes on for the molecular or cellular forms of storage. Various candidates include the RNA chains of molecules that help to form the proteins from the DNA, and the transmitter chemicals that link one nerve cell with another. Others envisage the memory records in more computer terms, being somehow electrically or chemically encoded among whole groups of cells or neural networks. Some, such as Karl Lashley, argue that attempts at localisation are futile, for the whole cortex seems to be involved.

For all our knowledge of cell structure and physiological function, our scientific understanding about the nature of memory remains the same – almost zero. The biologist J Z Young, always so careful and undogmatic, just naturally assumes it is a type of cellular storage, the simple correspondence of losing memory and loss of brain cells as we

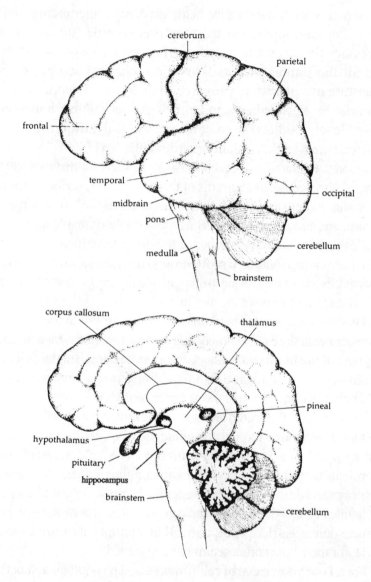

Figure 7a External and internal brain structure

get older speaking for itself. Equally distinguished people like John Eccles and Karl Popper have decided, on all the evidence of brain surgery, that memory belongs to a different order of things, a "World 2" or "World 3" over and above the physical world. Removing portions of the brain often has no effect on memory.

Then there is the interesting case of the Canadian surgeon, Wilder Penfield, who takes a position between the two. Both he and his distinguished mentor, Sir Charles Sherrington, were old-fashioned dualists about mind and brain. Using a low frequency electrical probe on the brain, Penfield became aware that a patient could distinguish clearly between what his probe effected, and what the conscious mind could control and decide. This to him was a clear indication that consciousness was not a direct function of the brain, rather that mind and brain were two different entities. Mind, the motivating force, was in some sense immaterial. Yet in spite of this, he believed that memory was somehow established in the material brain. Mind without memory sounds rather contradictory.

Penfield was responsible for providing so much new knowledge about brain function through his operations on epileptic patients. These can be done without general anaesthesia, for the cortex produces no pain sensations. It is rather the interpreter of pain sensations from other parts of the body. In addition to mapping the sensory and motor areas of the upper cortex using a 60 Hz probe, Penfield did come across some surprising sensations directly related to long-term memory. Using the probe on parts of the temporal cortex, patients sometimes experienced the clear memories of a musical concert they had once attended, and involving not just the music, but the whole emotional experience. As far as he could judge, removing the relevant cortical material did not remove such memories.

Most researchers make a clear distinction between short-term and long-term memory, or between conceptual and experiential memory. Probably most would agree that the cerebral cortex of neurons and axons constitute the short-term memory, all information from the external world being conveyed there, and presumably creating some sort

113

of chemical or electrical or magnetic impression. It also provides us with some conscious continuity from one moment to the next. But the long-term memories are seemingly at another level of storage, and these can be played back at the conscious level in the cerebral cortex. While we have some idea how to activate this physically, we have no understanding about where or how this material is stored.

Over the last ten years, the whole debate about the nature of memory has radically changed. The reason for this is that remarkable evidence has been obtained from people in all walks of life, and from all parts of the world, of deep subconscious memories involving experiences in previous centuries, and apparently unrelated to the existing life. Today, no longer bothered by academic ridicule and highly improbable rationalisations from orthodox scientists and doctors, educated people everywhere talk quite freely about their past lives and the exciting things they might once have been involved in.

Naturally, any scientist will have a healthy scepticism to new evidence that contradicts his most basic beliefs. But by virtue of the sheer volume of material coming through every day, and the amount of time necessary to try to refute just one significant statement, it is now an almost impossible task to challenge seriously what is going on. It also seems such a negative thing to do when the information is so intriguing, and of such natural human interest. Both Darwinians and Creationists seem very upset by this new trend – yet the last thing they want is to find any common cause.

As far as I can see from friends and acquaintances, much of this effort is personally beneficial, helping them to see their lives in a broader context, and making them less concerned about the failures of the current life, or about death. However professional hypnotherapists do warn that there are dangers exposing memories that the conscious mind may be unable to cope with; and I think it important that the regressions are done in a serious way with experienced people.

In the East, the reincarnation concept is something cultural, one of the taken-for-granted assumptions about life in general. For most of the twentieth century in the West, it has been primitive nonsense, both to the religious and non-religious. But over the last three decades, the change has been remarkable. We have all had opportunities to witness and assess directly the evidence from hypnotic regression; and the historical accuracy of much of the information, at very detailed levels, is there for all to see.

One of the first television presentations was by Arnall Bloxham in the 1970s, and among many other things, he managed to unearth new information about the persecution of the Jews in York in the twelfth century, and the existence of a crypt in a church thought not to have one. For me, the most remarkable documentary on these lines involved four Australian ladies who, under hypnosis in Australia, gave details of previous lives in Europe, and then travelled over to Europe to have their stories carefully analysed by local historians. In all cases, their meeting with the past proved a very emotional occasion.

One lady knew the fine details of a hospital in Blairgowrie, a small town in Scotland, as it was about a century-and-a-half ago. This particular story had a special personal interest for me, having visited the town three times during World War II to stay with my grandparents. Watching the television pictures, I could not recognise any of the town. Yet this lady was able to give very accurately the layout of the old hospital, the position of specific rooms, names of people - all of which could only be confirmed by the detailed research of a local expert.

Another was extremely conversant with a country district in France, and could speak the language easily under trance. A third was familiar with country life in Wiltshire, and supposedly had lived in a remote cottage. There, after much trudging through fields, they found a building in the right place but not of the right age. However, next to it was an older outhouse that fitted the period. In this, after removing various layers of material from the floor, they found the original stone floor, and on one of the stones was the pattern that she had previously drawn in Australia.

The evidence coming through is amusing, it is tragic, it is nostalgic, it is objective and historical. But there is little in it suggestive of an after-life. It is simply one life after another. So pronounced is this that some hypnotherapists believe that the moment one life ends, there is immediate incarnation into a new life. The *Tibetan Book of the Dead* suggests something on these lines. Most souls, through their fascination with sexual activity, are inevitably drawn back to biological life. It requires knowledge and control to avoid rebirth, and only the higher initiates are supposed to have the requisite ability.

According to most Western esoteric schools, there is both Earth life and Heaven life, and one suitably oscillates between the two. A period of rest and meditation and reflection is required by the soul after death; but eventually, new experiences are necessary or desirable to develop in different ways. It would seem that only Earth experience, the challenges and frustrations, the moral choices of freedom and duty, love and loneliness, only the unique expressions of these on this planet allow the soul to grow.

There is nothing too contradictory about these different versions of events. Roughly they suggest that the more developed and self-aware people spend less time on Earth overall, while those who have given little thought to fundamental matters spend more time. In this, one is not referring to social class and level of education, but to a basic approach to life and concern for others.

For those who broadly accept such a viewpoint, the evidence of past lives clearly presents no problem. The soul, containing all the records of past experience – knowing its own evolution – simply passes out of one body, and at some suitable stage joins another. Thus, as we know, the subconscious memory that is exposed under regression, is not necessarily related to the memories of parents and grandparents. Therefore, this would seem to rule out the possibility that one is reading just a genetic memory derived from the mother or father. These memories, including emotional content, can be very personal and intense. Some are so strong and difficult that they obstruct the current life; and one of the aims of hypnotherapy at the deep level is to encourage the subject to face the event again, and so come to terms with it.

To those who could never accept the concept of the immortal soul, there may or may not be a problem. There is no problem if the whole of hypnotic evidence is a fraud perpetrated on a gullible public. To some people, such as Jonathan Miller, hypnosis is a type of play-acting between two people. The subject wants to please the hypnotist, and suitably invents whatever may help the process. As for historical information, it was all read in a book sometime in the past, and just brought to consciousness. As for historical events only verified by obscure historical analysis, that would have to be in the area of deliberate fraud.

To the more serious investigator, there are important issues about the nature of memory and mind in the regression evidence. While it is not difficult to conceive of some form of cellular storage among the magnetically sensitive materials of the cell membrane, accurate and detailed memories in say the seventeenth century could only come through genetic transmission from a single male or female cell – which seems unlikely. Possibly the DNA is sufficiently complex to hold the information; and when it is replicated in billions of cells, there could be some resonance effect. But then, as previously stated, the genetic line does not generally relate to actual memories.

Yet how intrinsic are these far-memories to a specific individual? Edgar Cayce, the American prophet and seer who provided so much personal and general information over forty years through trance readings, seemed to have detailed knowledge of others going back many centuries. From what we know of the internal processes during his self-hypnotic sessions, he was not only delving into the mind and memory of an individual, but reading some more general Earth records. Rudolf Steiner also discusses at considerable length this general memory record of Earth events, maintaining one could extract the most arcane and personal information if in a suitable level of consciousness.

To Frederic Myers (discussed in more detail in Chapter 8), our memory floats like a cloud around us, with millions of subtle pathways of an electrical nature connecting specific memories to cells in the brain. Everything is very fluid - in keeping with the nature of memory - with new connections continuously forming through acts of will or through emotion. As we get older, or through injuries to the brain, we lose some of these connections, although all is preserved in the surrounding field. Somehow, according to Myers. this field is connected to the Great Memory, which is the common subconscious mind of all humanity. Our degree of access to the larger memory is a measure of our intellectual ability.

There are those today who perceive the geomagnetic field, and particularly the radiation belts, as memory centres for Earth activity. Now that we appreciate the subtle powers of magnetism to store and retrieve data, whether musical, pictorial, or verbal, this is not such an implausible idea. Possibly Rupert Sheldrake, with his *hypothesis of formative causation* involving some universal memory guiding organic form, may have had something like this in mind.

In the dream state, it seems quite probable that we could be linked in to some great environmental memory, particularly as the experiences often are so bizarre, or confused, or random. But this is less likely to be the case in hypnotic regression, which produces very specific experiences for the individual person. Randomly using some general memory, like idly perusing the books of a library, one is unlikely to focus on the same material over and over again.

In my own dreams, I have been for a long time intrigued by the physical pictures of places. These are far removed from the 3-dimensional perspective forms of the waking state. Thus, when I sometimes dream about my school or undergraduate life, I know which institution it is only from the context of the dream, not by the external appearance. In fact I have never had a dream with a physically recognisable building. Only the emotion associated with it seems to identify it. Presumably, this means that some of us do not carry over a memory of our conscious images into the dream life.

Is this connected with a universal memory? Or is there a much simpler explanation related to the differences between the left and right cerebral hemispheres. There does seem to be a general consensus that through dreams, or hypnosis, or meditation, or religious ritual, the right intuitive hemisphere becomes more dominant, and the conscious analytical constraints of the left hemisphere are by-passed. Thus, perhaps the right hemisphere, not having access to the normal conscious processes, cannot create a proper representation of buildings and general physical forms.

According to Julian Jaynes's thesis in *The Bicameral Mind*, it is only in the last two or three thousand years that the left hemisphere has become dominant. Prior to this, messages were received through the right hemisphere, and people acted on these promptings. We are aware today of such promptings among disturbed people, generally of a destructive nature. They are ordered to do something, and seemingly have no option but to obey. Yet at the other extreme, there are those who record very deep and meaningful messages by such means. This form of communication, discussed in chapter 8, provides much food for thought.

It is doubtful that these speculative ideas, and the new regression evidence, can immediately contribute anything towards a *scientific* understanding of the nature of memory. Scientists are struggling with the very elementals of the subject – the short-term conscious memory. Not having made any intelligible impact on the most obvious problems, not having found any unique storage unit within the brain for short-term memory, not having been able to relate specific neuronal networks to specific memory patterns, the last thing the professional researcher can be interested in is this most unusual evidence now coming through.

But in the longer term, there could be an impact. The sheer barrenness of current research should encourage scientists to stand back a little from the problem. This is not to disparage what has been done, because negative knowledge is important. All the obvious avenues must be tried if only for elimination. But often it has proved that the unusual, the curious anomaly, gives that slight clue which leads on to new understanding. There is certainly reason to question whether any cellular or molecular storage theory of long-term memory is likely to be useful. As with radio waves, we often seem to pluck information out of the general background. Are we in fact doing this all the time with our own electrical waves that resonate with similar frequencies in the geomagnetic field?

There is surely some broader picture we should be studying. The close relationship of the waveforms of the brain and geomagnetic resonances looks too curious to be coincidental. The lowest Schumann frequency between the ionosphere and the earth's surface of about 7.8 Hz is just below the 8-12 Hz alpha range of the brain, and just above the 4-7 theta range. The alpha range reflects a relaxed, near-sleep state, and the theta range is associated with trance and abnormal states. However, while electromagnetics may be involved in mental communication between two people, or in hypnotic regression, or between the subconscious and some general Earth memory, this is hardly likely to account for the personal memory built up through the everyday experiences of this life.

There are though some specific ideas about memory that may be worthy of some consideration. If Indian philosophers, and those who try to translate their ideas to the Western mind, have some specific views on soul structure, they should have something interesting to say about the nature of human memory. So, if we go to someone like Rudolf Steiner, who probably had more to say on more subjects than any other man who has ever existed (his works run into hundreds of volumes), combine it with a few ideas from Edgar Cayce, and add in some of the more speculative notions of modern physics, one might begin to conceptualise human memory along the following lines.

As far as I understand the esoteric view, the cosmos is to be regarded, not so much as a Great Mind, but a Great Memory. Within the universal akasa, or aether, everything that has ever happened is eternally recorded. For those who develop the mind through the meditational disciplines of yoga, these records can be directly studied, and the most arcane material becomes available. By this means, for instance, Steiner provides quite a lengthy account of the early life of Jesus, including a period spent among the Essenes – seemingly corroborated by the Dead Sea Scrolls.

In his more scientific moments, Steiner describes *akasa*, the substance of space-time, as a form of negative energy, the inverse or complement of physical matter. The soul material, and the psychic centres, are variants of akasa – different forms of negative energy.

Curiously, soon after putting forward this idea, Paul Dirac was saying something very similar to physicists, with the whole of space filled with electrons of negative mass. From this starting point, he successfully predicted the existence of the positron, a particle of positive charge and mass.

The negative-energy aether implies a complementary energy domain, a shadow-world to the physical, and interacting with it through the forces of electromagnetism. This then would suggest a possible view of memory which is just outside current scientific perspectives. From the lack of positive progress in memory research, that is surely where one might expect to find something. So, with general Earth records within the universal akasa, and individual memories within the major centres of the psyche, we perhaps have the beginnings of a rationalisation. We are told, furthermore, that the daily experiences are first stored and analysed in the cerebral centres, and then move down to lower centres where they can only be accessed by special methods. On this basis, the soul-body contains all the material from one life to another, thus accounting for the unusual memory material exposed under hypnotic regression.

Although speculative, I find nothing implausible about the above – either from correspondence with the evidence, or in my own internal sense about what is happening, or in the light of modern physical theories. It does not of course provide us with any detail about how the pictures are stored, but that is surely not a very significant matter. In our own technology, for instance, magnetic forces are used in a great variety of ways to store all sorts of information, from pictures to music to language to ideas. In our present state of ignorance, what we need are some rudimentary ideas about the nature and flow of information between the major centres of the psyche, rather than the precise method of storage.

As for actual evidence of the existence of the soul-body, the most convincing comes from the near-death states involving descriptions of operations by patients from a vantage point away from and above the body. Doctors have been aware of this for a century or more. Even hard-line materialists are now prepared to concede that these are common and real experiences - although rationalising them in hallucinogenic terms through lack of oxygen to the brain. A few European hospitals have made systematic studies of patients who seem to have died, carefully interviewing them directly after the experience. These accounts have many common factors; and the clear, calm, conscious observations of events surrounding the physical body on the operating table does definitely seem to imply the existence of some other entity that is not subject to physical deterioration, and able to function independently of the body.

In terms of our discussion of human memory, note that these experiences are not only viewed from the soul-body, *they are committed to memory at the same time*. Therefore, even though there may be short-term physical memories within the cerebral matter, the experiential memory, and the understanding of the memory, must be within the soul-body itself. For all his important work on brain function, I think we must discount Penfield's theory of immaterial mind and material memory. It is a natural, common-sense view that memory, and the understanding of memory that we call the mind, cannot exist without each other; and this view is reinforced by the near-death experiences.

For those looking for something more definite about the nature of human memory, the best I can do is quote from Edgar Cayce's biography *There is a river* by Thomas Sugrue. A certain Arthur Lammers, of general philosophical disposition, decided he wanted something more than medical diagnoses from the Cayce subconscious: he wanted some answers to basic psychological questions. For those sympathetic to what has so far been discussed, the following quotation is of more than considerable interest. There is certainly nothing in it that conflicts with present knowledge, and much that corresponds with our intuitive sense of things.

'Now, it's like this. The conscious mind is the record of this life. Just as an emotion is the experience of a single moment, so the conscious mind is the record of a single life. This conscious mind

is located in the pituitary gland. That, at least, is its focal point – the gland has a purely physical function also.

The thoughts go from the conscious to the imaginative, or introspective, mind, which is seated in the pineal gland. There the thoughts are compared with all that has gone before that is in any way related to them, and when this is done, the thoughts – properly conditioned and judged – pass on to the subconscious, or soul mind, which is seated, with its spirit, just above the heart. There the thoughts are kept as a record, and as they are constructive they quicken the spirit and lower the barrier between the soul and the pure essence of life. As they are destructive they are rejected, but kept as a record, and as they are repeated they build up the barrier between the soul and the spirit and dim the radiance of the life essence that shines through the subconscious to the imaginative, and by refraction, or hunch, intuition, and yearning, into the conscious.'

To me, this looks like an intelligent starting point for some new theorising about the nature of memory.

Chapter Eight

Psychical Research

In 1986, the distinguished journal *Physics Today* published a most unusual article on the psychical research and spiritualist beliefs of some of the most famous physicists at the end of the nineteenth century. This was presented in a factual and historical way, not with the dramatics and ridicule that we have naturally come to expect from most other scientific journals dealing with such matters.

I hasten to add that such a presentation was not out of character for this journal which has an excellent reputation for open discussion and breadth of view. Among several unusual things they have published are the experiments of David Cohen and others about the magnetic field of the human body. Most careful measurements were made of this, either screening out or compensating for the geomagnetic field, and using the most advanced equipment of the SQUID super-conducting magnetometer. By and large, those in the life sciences regard any such work on vertebrate fields as being a form of *vitalism*, a view belonging to some primitive age.

The author of the article, Janet Oppenheim, a professor of history, concentrated on four distinguished scientists: Lord Rayleigh, J.J. Thomson, Sir William Crookes, and Sir Oliver Lodge. She quotes Lord Rayleigh:

'A decision of the existence of mind independent of ordinary matter must be far more important than any scientific discovery could be, or rather would be the most important possible scientific discovery.'

Figure 8a Lord Rayleigh, J.J. Thomson,
Sir William Crookes, Sir Oliver Lodge

And again:

'I have never thought the materialist view possible, and I look to a power beyond what we see, and to a life in which we may at least hope to take part.'

Rayleigh succeeded Clerk Maxwell as the Cavendish professor of experimental physics in Cambridge, and he in turn was succeeded by J.J. Thomson. Maxwell, one of our greatest scientists, formulated the mathematical theory of electromagnetism that has stood the test of time for over a hundred years. Maxwell, like Faraday before him, had rather strict religious views, and would not have been sympathetic to any experiments related to unusual psychical phenomena.

Rayleigh made important contributions to wave theory in sound and electromagnetics, and discovered the element argon. J.J. Thomson moved forward into atomic and quantum physics, and discovered the electron. Both joined the Society for Psychical Research (SPR), and carefully and sympathetically investigated evidence for telepathy. Crookes and Lodge went much further, and, through their own experimentation, became convinced spiritualists.

Crookes was a free-lance chemist and physicist, and his many and varied discoveries eventually brought him a knighthood and the Order of Merit. He made contributions to molecular physics, radiation, metallurgy, vacuum technology, dyeing, sewage disposal, beet sugar, and discovered the element thallium. In his psychical research, he set up careful experiments in materialisation with famous mediums of the day, and was sure he ruled out all possibility of fraud by connecting the medium to an electrical circuit to prevent any movement. The severe criticism he received from contemporary scientists caused him to give up this work in middle life; and only towards the end of his life after his wife died did he resume the interest. While Rayleigh and Thomson reserved judgement about the evidence for life-after-death, Crookes believed the case had been proved.

Oliver Lodge had a distinguished academic career, although much less orthodox than Rayleigh and Thomson. After helping his father in his pottery business for many years, he was in his twenties before he received any formal scientific training. In spite of this, he became professor of physics at Liverpool when he was thirty. He made significant contributions to wireless telegraphy, and was one of those who helped to formulate the classical electromagnetic equations which have been somewhat erroneously termed the Maxwell Equations. Maxwell, with his treatise on electricity and magnetism, did provide the groundwork for them; but others like Lodge simplified the concepts to something more manageable. Lodge also contributed to the Special Theory of Relativity with experiments designed to measure the effect of the ether. The negative nature of all such experiments clarified the situation, and led on to relativistic thinking.

Oliver Lodge came slowly to a spiritualist viewpoint through his fifty-year association with the Society for Psychical Research. He had no interest in the physical phenomena that intrigued Crookes, and in fact warned him of the dangers of fraud. After some early experiments in thought transference, he turned his attention to automatic scripts obtained from mediums. These could be studied at leisure, and very elaborate tests were devised for the communicators. His final certainty about the after-life came through the death of his son Raymond during the first world war, and through subsequent communications. Such experiences only reinforced his lifelong Christian beliefs.

It does help I suppose to have a certain outlook on life, certain images of interacting minds, that would allow for the possibility of spiritualist communication. It also helps to discover, through science, that most of what goes on in the world is not registered by any of our senses, thereby causing us to create very selective pictures. In particular, as regards electromagnetic energy, we only register about one octave - the visual spectrum - of the eighty or so octaves that we know something about. Thus when I first came across spiritualist ideas, and found that they actually did think in these terms, I was keen to know a little more.

My actual experience of psychical research is fairly meagre, and no one has ever asked me to join a society or study group. Friends at college assured me they had witnessed materialisations, but nothing like that has ever come my way. However the little contact I have had has always held something of interest, and some of the literature is intriguing, to say the least. The Bishop Pike account of his experiences concerning the death of his son in Cambridge, the communications that totally changed his life and thought, and then the subsequent saga in the Sinai Desert with his second wife, were major talking points in the academic world in the 1970s. Prior to these experiences, the Bishop had only contempt for so-called psychic matters.

My earliest experience was when I was asked to play the piano for a major public demonstration in Chelmsford in the late 1940s. For me, it was just a way of earning a little money, involving some introductory classical music and one hymn, as far as I can remember. The proceedings took place on a summer's evening; and without going into a trance, but using some Rudolf Steiner (the first time I had heard that name) technique of conscious clairvoyance, the speaker discussed in some detail the lives of four people in the audience, spending about twenty minutes on each. The level of detail discussed could only have meant that the session was either completely fraudulent, or basically what it purported to be. At the end of the meeting, one of those involved came up to the platform, and I was able to overhear a conversation about how she was passing the hall that evening, and for some unknown reason, just decided to come in. As far as I am aware, only the lady, the speaker and his assistant, and myself were aware of what was said. So that seemed to rule out fraud.

Looking back on this demonstration, it was probably the most convincing of my life. And the fact that I had zero knowledge of all those involved probably helped to reinforce this. As soon as one gets to know any other person in this world, it gets progressively easier to make intelligent guesses about their life.

Those who have dipped into the literature on the subject will find nothing surprising about the above. William James, for instance, had long conversations with old colleagues who had passed on through the help of a Mrs Piper, and both the character and everyday details of the conversations were such as to cause him to express the wish that he had begun to study such matters earlier in life. Anyone who has read the major works of psychology and philosophy of William James could never accuse him of gullibility.

His experience was not dissimilar to my own. For many years, I did not meet anyone interested in the subject, and never bothered to seek out those actively engaged in psychical research. But like many people, I much enjoyed hearing about Rosemary Brown and the music she was supposedly taking down from Liszt and his contemporaries. She told us that Liszt physically appeared to her, talked naturally, and told her precisely what notes to write down. She could play the piano a little, but had no knowledge or experience of composition. Yet the pieces dictated to her caught the style perfectly of several of the romantic composers. If it had to happen to anyone, how appropriate that such a friendly and unassuming person as Rosemary should receive the music.

But then I met a friendly and unassuming person who kindly allowed me a few "Mrs Piper" sessions. Sometimes she went into a deep trance, sometimes not. Under trance, there was generally a slow beginning with mundane greetings, and bits of inconsequential material. But as the session progressed, the information became more specific. Sometimes I came away disappointed with the level of discussion - although playing the tape through a month or two later, it tended to be rather more meaningful. One of the things she picked up at a very early stage were problems that my second daughter was experiencing far away in America, and which I had no inkling of. In fact, having visited her not long before the session in question, and found everyone well, I simply did not believe it. Only years later was this confirmed.

Throughout this period, there was no suggestion of proselytizing or indoctrination; and she and her husband were always willing to cooperate with some electromagnetic experiments I was making at the time. I have the impression that most people experimenting in this field believe that one day, as our electronic engineering gets more subtle, secure channels of communication will be opened up, in contrast to the difficult uncertain methods through the human cerebral systems. There are in fact scientists and technologists today who are quite convinced that this type of communication is already taking place through tape recorders and mobile phones.

As with William James, I could truthfully say that here was something of great psychological interest. Just what it was, that is the real question. Whether it was a form of telepathy, communicating with spirits, using the intuitive right-brain, picking up fragments from some universal memory, or hopeful guessing, that is for each person to decide.

To study the best evidence for the continuity of consciousness after death (there is absolutely no point in the study of mediocre or bad evidence) is an immense undertaking, requiring a lifetime of study. I have little sympathy for those scientists, always so conscious of orthodoxy and desirous of avoiding anything that might displease the hierarchy, who come on to our TV screens with their immediate judgements, hardly having given the subject five minutes thought, and never having made any attempt at scientific investigation. If they do make a little effort, they seem to expect miracles straight away; and when these are not immediately forthcoming, they are happy to join the mob, and pronounce it all a fraud - as of course they have always been encouraged to believe.

Frederic Myers did study the best evidence, and finally produced his one great work on the subject - *Human Personality and its Survival of Bodily Death*. Just for doing this, one can find many scornful references in modern psychological literature about Myers, and in fact of anyone who put real effort into this subject. Such scorn, based not on study but on simple ignorance and hearsay, is sustained by this unholy alliance of Creationists, Darwinians, and academic psychologists, who want us to believe that all psychics are corrupting, fraudulent, and exploitive. And when reinforced by people like Freud, who freely borrowed from their ideas with his *id-ego-superego* thesis, and Einstein who knew nothing about the subject, all their dutiful followers naturally take the same line. Even the police forces of America now make serious use of their services.

No doubt there are fraudulent operators, just as there are in most branches of life. Because of pressure to succeed, and pressure to win research grants, fraud is becoming quite a problem in scientific work, particularly in the life sciences where results are seldom cut-and-dried. But at the really serious levels of investigation, such as those conducted by the SPR, spiritualists have held the attention of some of the most interesting people - the physicists previously mentioned, Lord Dowding the Air Marshall who directed the Battle of Britain, William James the philosopher, Bishop Pike the theologian, writers such as Conan Doyle and Rosamund Lehmannn. Even the co-founder of modern evolutionary theory, Alfred Russell Wallace, was a dedicated spiritualist right to the end of his days. Altogether a very broad church indeed.

Many modern scientists, whilst claiming to be open-minded, have taken up a philosophical stance which more or less precludes the possibility of life-after-death notions having any validity. There is no soul to survive, life consisting of carbon-based molecules and genes and cells. Everything is built up from the bottom, and the higher levels of control that we call the mind evolve out of more complex arrangements of these tiny elements of matter.

There is nothing intrinsically wrong in making such assumptions; and science can only progress by suitably compartmentalising particular aspects for special study. By all means, let us see where we can get by taking the atomic and molecular and genetic thesis as far as we can. By doing this, we may become better aware of the natural boundaries of materialist studies. But let us realise at the same time that these are working assumptions; and as we pursue deeper into psychological areas, it is very difficult to conceive how they are directly relevant. Scientifically, the whole psychological area is still wide open; and it is a form of ignorance to suggest that some atomic explanation is just around the corner.

In the sense of dealing with more abstract notions of force and field and wave and frequency, it is natural that physicists and mathematicians should be the more interested in psychical research. Those in the life sciences, the biochemists and physiologists, show little interest in Newtonian mechanics, let alone the electromagnetics of Faraday,

Maxwell and Tesla. Seldom will you find in a standard physiological text a discussion of the basic structural forces of the body; and nowhere will you find anything about the magnetic fields and forces associated with nerve currents. Psychical research is very interested in such matters.

With religious objectors, there are quite different problems. Among other things, we are dealing with forms of church orthodoxy, and the mental conditioning of this orthodoxy. There is a view of an ultimate being who has very strict views on most things, and most people. I have to agree with the Gnostics and Charles Darwin that in the world he is supposed to have created, in his likes and dislikes, and in his strong sense of retribution, he is not a very appealing being. In fact, if he is as bad as the evangelicals make out (only those completely obedient to a certain strict biblical view survive), one has to conclude that the moral sense of this being is definitely primitive.

In a historical context, it has always seemed to me that only a rather primitive religion came down to us through the Church. In the fourth century, the superstitious Constantine decided he had won a battle with the help of the sign of the Cross, and in quite a short time, Christianity was elevated from a small sect to a universal religion. It had to be a religion for everyman, not for the more philosophical. And so it was suitably constructed, relying heavily on the miraculous aspect, and the intoning of absolute statements of belief. The more thoughtful and esoteric aspects survived only through heretical groups like the Gnostics.

My understanding is that spiritualists do have a Christian vision, but something broader than the Church, and part of a liberal tradition. Certainly I have found more open-mindedness among them than most other organised groups. They can accept the reality of the communion of saints, not because of inherited belief, but because of the evidence. They make no attempt to coerce or indoctrinate, and are happy to cooperate with any serious investigator, whatever his particular prejudices.

But I do have problems with the evidence they present. At a rather mundane level, one has to wonder why so many of the world's mysteries are not immediately cleared up. Taking a particular issue that I once took more than a little interest in, what really did happen to Christopher Marlowe after 1593? He doesn't seem to be the Christopher Morley stabbed in a tavern brawl. Was he the man of the same name who turned up at Valladolid in Spain in the 1620s? Was he exiled because of his Catholic sympathies, or his atheistic tendencies, or his friendship with Sir Walter Rayleigh? Did he continue to write plays while abroad, sending them on to the Globe Theatre by special courier, only to see the theatre manager pass them off as his own? What you, Will!

We all have mysteries that we want to know the answer to. Eileen Garrett, so admired by academics because of her openness to scientific studies, did clarify a few things about the R101 airship disaster. Edgar Cayce, under hypnosis, gave us some apparently new knowledge about earlier civilisations, including the dating of the pyramids which is now being taken seriously by archaeologists. Among the thousands of lectures given by Rudolf Steiner, most now published in English and German, we have a fairly extensive account of the early life of Jesus among the Essenes. Dealing with more scientific matters, the *Mahatma Letters*, supposedly transmitted to Madame Blavatsky by two Himalayan sages, provide long and complex answers to Western-type questions prepared by the editor of the Indian Times, Alfred Sinnett.

Little of this is presented as personal communications from souls who have passed on. Rather it is based on the idea that, somewhere in space-time, there is a permanent record of everything that has ever happened, a tree of knowledge. Presumably the orthodox religious will continue to believe that we touch this at our peril.

There is a Buddhist argument that we in the West have misunderstood psychical phenomena. Viewing the human psyche as a system of linked entities, with a gradual shedding of the lower ones as we move into higher realms, they sometimes argue that only those who have died prematurely can be contacted, and then presumably only for a short time. Most of spiritualism they suggest is contact with the dying shells of the lower self, and which may be completely at odds with the higher self. Western spiritualists would answer that the level of contact, and level of information, is dependent on the spiritual state of the medium.

Much of worth is available to a few, and much nonsense comes to many.

The Society for Psychical Research, formed in Cambridge in 1882, and its American counterpart, have conducted their experiments in a strict scientific way. It has always been a highly academic body, with standards that some think are more rigorous than major scientific journals. For much of its life, it has tried to distinguish between what could be explained by telepathy between living people, and what seemed only explicable on a life-after-death basis. They have worked very closely with psychics of the highest integrity such as Eileen Garrett and Mrs Leonard and Mrs Piper who were quite open-minded about the nature of their special abilities.

Part of their study has involved the construction of sophisticated literary puzzles using mediums in several countries, and relating to extremely recondite material from ancient Greek culture that only a very few specialists would have any knowledge of. Partial information comes to each medium; and when put together, these *cross-correspondences* should make complete sense. To many of the highly educated members of the SPR, such tests have produced very strong evidence of communication with departed souls, rather than telepathy between living people.

Few people, and particularly scientists, have much inclination to study the fine details of these tests today, however convincing to an earlier generation. But they would naturally appeal to people like Frederick Myers who lectured in classics at Cambridge University, was a poet and notable literary critic, and one of the founders of the SPR. Myers both helped to formulate the tests, and later after his death, to fill in the details, supposedly from the other side.

People today want something much more direct, and which helps them to make sense of the life they are leading. If there is another life, a continuing life elsewhere, what are the conditions of existence, do we come back, do we have choice, does individuality survive, is there a judgement of some kind, are there other types of matter to provide an environment, why is communication so difficult, why do the religious here oppose it so much? Many groups have given rather convincing answers to these questions - followers of Swedenborg and Rudolf Steiner, theosophists and Rosicrucians, and the spiritualists themselves. But with the great influence of the scientific movement against all such thinking, the main mass of humanity has yet to be won over.

If I had to name one document, one reasonably complete and concise statement of the spiritualist view, I would be inclined to recommend the book first published in 1932 containing the automatic writings of Geraldine Cummins entitled *The Road to Immortality*. In the following brief description of this book, I will avoid the tiresome use of the word "supposed", and assume things are as they say they are.

The circumstances surrounding the book are rather intriguing. In the foreword by Sir Oliver Lodge, we first read that

'Miss Geraldine Cummins is a fairly well-known amateur trance-writer: that is one who through withdrawal of consciousness is controlled so as to write on matters outside his or her knowledge.'

A very odd, half-hearted statement indeed! Now Miss Cummins, so we are told, did not know anything of Frederick Myers prior to her writing sessions supervised by her friend Miss Gibbes. Note that this automatic writing comes very quickly, and it is necessary to have someone organising the pages. Lodge makes very clear that he was suspicious of the claim that Myers was communicating through Geraldine Cummins. So he went to his tried and tested, *professional* medium, Mrs Osborne Leonard, to ask his son on the other side whether it was true that Myers was using Miss Cummins. He said that it was true, and then Myers himself confirmed it - with a proviso that it was rather hard work getting the ideas through. Lodge concludes the foreword with the following statement.

'I believe this to be a genuine attempt to convey approximately true ideas, through an amanuensis of reasonable education,

characterised by a willingness for devoted service, and of transparent honesty.'

Again, not a ringing endorsement; but a suitable cautionary note from a distinguished scientist, and much preferable to definitive claims. Thoughtful people are not looking for absolute truth or verification, and realise that it is probably impossible to conduct tests about life-after-death that are completely foolproof. Each experience or event that points in that direction will be unique, and not replicable.

During the course of the book, Myers explains various modes of communicating with someone like Geraldine Cummins, and whom he regarded as an *interpreter* rather than a medium. He says it is difficult, although not impossible, to convey actual words. Sometimes he uses a specific psychic centre of the interpreter; other times he conveys a general image. In some complex way through the mental systems of the interpreter, the thought or message or picture gets translated into the written word. It is of interest, although open to various interpretations, that certain words that only Myers had ever used such as *polyzoic* and *metetheric* do appear in the text.

The intelligent question to ask all through a book like this is whether or not what is said about other forms of life on other planes makes general sense. The scientists have discovered nothing that makes sense of all our strivings in this world, and provide neither comfort nor purpose. Rather, many of them go right out of their way to preach that there is no purpose, no freewill, and that all is either random or pre-determined. Does then what Myers says, or what Geraldine Cummins says, give us a picture of life and the universe which is plausible, reasonable, hopeful, and something that, deep down, we could sense as probably being true?

Many of us, while being in awe of the extraordinary and magnificent universe around us, feel that many things are essentially wrong with life on earth. It often seems more of a prison than a paradise. We are afflicted with so much illness, so many natural disasters, we have to eat other animals, there is great anguish and anxiety trying to keep a family going in a civilised way. The early Christian Gnostics believed that this world was fundamentally flawed, and under malign influences. If there is some wider context in which all is seen as ultimately fair and reasonable, then we have to be interested. If some concept is natural to our way of thinking, then one hopes to build on it.

In little over a hundred pages, Frederic Myers presents us with an account of how life may be, in a wider context. We currently exist in what is considered the lowest plane of the cosmos, the plane of matter. In terms of living things, Myers says this is the slowest vibratory rate. The highest, or seventh plane is the ultimate communion with the source of creation, and presumably the eternal paradise envisaged by the main religions of the world.

Much of what Myers describes concerns the intermediate planes, and presumably where most of us will spend most of our time. In fact, he states that there are many Christian mystics and Buddhist adepts who, in their strictness of view, mistakenly think they have arrived at their final destination on the fourth plane. To Myers, it is not just a certain goodness or righteousness or love, but a special form of wisdom, an openness of mind to explore all possibilities, that leads on to the final state of Nirvana.

Myers concentrates mainly on the third and fourth planes. After disentangling our soul-body from the physical, we arrive at the second plane, or Hades. This is a temporary resting place after death, which in most cases is a pleasant and tranquil experience - really quite the opposite of the birth experience. The soul rests within a veil in a state of peaceful quiescence, watching in a detached way fragments of the past life. This is a place of rest, reflection, reassessment to which we return several times on the upward journey through the planes.

Most of us move on quickly to what the spiritualists call the Summerlands, with an environment and scenery similar to our own, but without the imperfections. We may apparently choose to return to the earth level for a great variety of good or bad reasons - Myers has few of the reservations that many spiritualists have about the reincarnation concept.

Above the earth plane, the mind, and its natural desires, become much stronger, and the third plane may not satisfy these for long. But those who developed an ordered existence on earth can be quite comfortable for long periods of time, particularly as there are no physical illnesses to contend with. There, they can create their own environment similar to that on earth just with the power of the mind.

However, he does refer to this as the "plane of illusion", and Oliver Lodge tells us he asked Myers whether that was what he really meant. Myers gives the following answer.

'In time, such peace becomes wearisome; for no actual progress, either up or down, can be made in that delightful region of dream. Picture it for a moment: you live in surroundings that resemble those you knew on earth. You are, it is true, freed from money worries, free from the need to earn your daily bread. ... It is indeed as if you lived in a pond, and soon you weary of the limitations of that calm, unruffled sheet of water. You yearn for struggle, effort, ecstasy; you long for wide horizons. The call of the road has come to you again. In short, you are anxious to make further progress either up or down.'

He refers several times to a mythical Tom Jones, the ordinary decent person, who needs to be treated very gently after death, and often stays at the third level. He makes the obvious but important point that Tom Jones, if he suddenly became a great seer at that stage, would no longer be Tom Jones. Our mental evolution, like the physical evolution on this planet, is a very lengthy process. Most of us will be like children on a higher plane.

The cruel man can indulge himself as much as he wishes. However, it is a great torment when a craving cannot be fully satisfied, and a return to earth is often preferable. But Myers makes little of any sense of judgement on passing over. All one's past life can be viewed as desired; and for those who have lived thoughtful lives, this can be very pleasing. Obviously if this is not the case, it could be disturbing, although the hardened criminal might not be bothered.

He maintains that human memory, which is the essential source of our individuality, is separate from the brain, and is carried over at death with the double-body. He describes the memory in terms of finer material floating around the body, and with millions of threads making connections with individual cells in the brain. These connections are formed by the will and strong emotion. After death, he says the soul does not have such connections, although the memory field can be perused at any time. Therefore, in communicating with the earth-plane, he would not necessarily have detailed factual knowledge of past events, but would have to look them up as required.

There is also the Great Memory, or Book of Life, but only a few know how to access it on our plane. It is not akin to a factual encyclopaedia, but contains the emotional essence of all that has ever happened. This may explain why we seldom get historical conundrums solved. In all he says about memory, he gives the impression that facts, as we conceive them, are of little importance compared with the thought and emotional content behind them. Many writers and historians would agree with this.

Describing the fourth plane, he refers to the "breaking of the image". This is when really new things happen, there is a vitality quite distinct from the dream-state of the previous level. It is a world of form and colour, of great fluidity, and vibrating at an unimaginable speed. Like souls congregate together to form a Group-Soul, presumably akin to a monastic community. Pain and pleasure are once more experienced, but in a refined, heightened, intensified way. He says that he can build a likeness to himself, beam that to a friend, and control it instantly. He is learning to live within and without form.

Moving to the fifth stage, he tells us that this involves a type of death and a brief return to the Hades retreat. "Flame" is the symbol of this plane; and the soul-body, which up to this level has remained a reflection of the earth-body, gives way to forms that are self-created. In others words, we gain direct control over the way we present ourselves. The individual soul, together with all the companion souls, create a great fire of emotional form. Many supposedly cannot make the transition.

'There are numerous fanatical Christians who, though they led lives of rectitude on earth, committed certain intellectual sins. These might be summed up in the phrase "rigidity of thought", "an outlook limited by fanaticism"..... Now if the soul is to pass from the Fourth to the Fifth stage, he must first shake off, cast from him, any dogma, any special earthly outlook which has shaped his mentality, which confines it.'

At this level, there are no gaps of consciousness, no sleep states. It is a time of severe discipline, of vastly increased thought and feeling, and which may be communicated occasionally to a special being on earth. All in the group-soul must attain a certain level before passing to the sixth stage where the white light of pure reason and pure thought reigns, without any trace of earthly emotion. Knowledge of good and evil, and what lies beyond, are theirs.

The final stage does not involve the annihilation of the individual, as the Buddhists believe, but an existence outside the material universe, beyond time and space. Many are called, but few are chosen.

'Understand, therefore, that the Universe is only unreal so long as you dwell within its confining web, within form. It is real when you are free from it, and are able from Out Yonder to survey it as a whole and to know it as an act of pure thought.'

Throughout this exposition, there is much talk of finer matter, and Geraldine Cummins notes in her introduction that this anticipated the discovery of the world of subatomic particles. However Myers, who died in 1901, indicates that he had been following world events, including the Great War, and would presumably be conversant with scientific developments. Not that this is much of an issue because the concept of subtler matter occurs frequently in ancient Indian writings. According to Myers, we have a body, derived from the *double* of our earth-body, up to the fourth stage; and, for want of a better term, this is composed of fine *ether* particles. However, he would prefer the physicists to allocate suitable particle names.

Throughout his exposition, there is a certain humanity that I think many thoughtful people today will warm to. He is in fact quite critical of ascetics and mystics who encourage their followers towards a world-renouncing path. In the chapter entitled "Happiness", he makes the following sensible and practical observations.

'A desire for money in moderation is a virtue, for it happens to be a desire to become a complete man, and, through such completion and its resultant content, to benefit others.

Happiness comes through effort; through a wise and controlled indulgence in the pleasures of the senses; through athletic activities for the perfecting of the body; through study for the development of the mind; and through toleration or a charitable outlook. The development of these leads to the cultivation of the spirit.

True happiness will be found by the average man in the constant and wise use of all his talents, all his powers - of body, senses, mind, and spiritual perception.'

Several times he stresses the concept of wisdom, a word that, unlike love, has not been polluted by our modern culture. He defines wisdom as "right judgement concerning the truth", and this is central to our mental evolution.

'Consider, then, the significance of "wisdom". For, clearly, within that lofty word resides the highest love between man and woman, intellectual love, compassion, faith, and last but not least, the power of vision. All these are possessed by the man or woman who rightly judges truth. And, on whatever plane your soul or the soul of the beloved is evolving, be assured that wisdom is the primary urge which causes this soul to choose to go up rather

than down, to select the finer life, the greater reality, rather than existence in denser forms, in more material worlds.'

After describing the various planes, he deals briefly with freewill, the conscious and subconscious mind, sleep, hypnosis, telepathy, and communication of thought. On the subject of freewill, he is rather more reserved than William James (chapter 5), suggesting that, given the long evolution of the mind through countless experiences, the path chosen at any point is almost inevitable. More important than the path is our emotional response to all the difficulties and challenges that come our way.

He finishes with a short piece on the concept of God, *who is greater than love.*

'It is strange to me that God should be described as loving and good, or as jealous and vengeful. He is none of these. He is the inevitable, the "Omega" of all life. But He is neither evil nor good, neither cruel nor kind. He is the Purpose behind all purpose. ... He is the Idea behind the myriad worlds, behind the unnumbered Universes.'

Myers told Lodge that he couldn't be sure his communication was always exact, although on the whole it fairly represented what he wanted to say. Lodge considered the material to be true to the character of Myers, and distinct from other communications of Miss Cummins on esoteric matters, which produced *Scripts of Cleophas*, *Paul in Athens*, *The Great Days of Ephesus,* and containing material that her conscious mind would have no knowledge of. In the Myers case, we are given to understand that she writes as an agnostic, with no prior acquaintance of psychical research or theosophy.

It would seem that Oliver Lodge was surprised by the whole episode, generally suspicious, but finally giving it a reluctant endorsement. He couldn't understand why Myers had chosen to communicate with someone quite unknown to him. Later experiments concerning some *cross-reference* testing between Mrs Osborne and Geraldine Cummins is printed in the book, and seems to have reassured him.

'The accounts which Myers goes on to give of the fourth, fifth, sixth, and seventh states are remarkable, but I see no reason to dissent from the view that they are the kind of ideas which Frederic W.H.Myers may by this time have been able to form.'

To those familiar with Indian ideas, with Yoga, with theosophy or anthroposophy, Myer's conception of the evolution of human life will represent a natural progression of ideas, fitting in nicely with multi-system concepts of mind and body. To open-minded agnostic scientists, they will probably be considered worthy of interest; and, in terms of field and energy and particles, not that far distant from the latest speculations in physics. Everything in physics today is in a state of great fluidity; and when Myers talks of finer matter, or universes within universes, or instant communication at a distance, there is nothing too surprising about any of that. For science fiction writers, it could be all rather too mundane.

Yet those things that obviously bother Oliver Lodge, such as the "plane of illusion", will continue to bother many of us today. What does it mean to say that experiences in the lower planes are illusory? All experience, surely, is real to the experiencer. Things may seem a bit hazy in childhood; but when we enter the adult world, have to manipulate it, design machines, earn money, educate children, accept great responsibilities, then the reality is overwhelming.

That said, there is a sense in which scientists have changed many preconceptions, and even they talk about our view of matter as being in some sense illusory. It is easily possible to conceive that some other being, in some other vibratory state, and receptive to a different spectral range, would view the world quite differently, and not even be aware of the protein molecules that make up the human being. However, that doesn't make our world illusory in any philosophical sense. It simply means that, at any particular level, or vibrational range, we have only a partial view. Presumably our sense organs are intelligently selective to allow us to concentrate on specific aspects of life that are vital to our survival.

Some would say that Myer's account leaves too many questions unanswered. But spiritualists would answer that there is large body of literature filling in many of the details, particularly about the third plane. Emanuel Swedenborg, a distinguished mining engineer before becoming a world figure, and Andrew Jackson Davies, an American mystic, are two that have provided lengthy accounts of experiences initiated from this side; and there are many complementary accounts from the other side coming through automatic writing.

Plato, in the *Phaedo*, tells us of a fairer world, with landscapes and plants of wonderful colour. Just as air is finer than water, and ether than air, this environment is that much superior to earth. The precious gems of earth provide just a glimpse of the pure materials in the world to come. In these temperate regions, devoid of disease and decay caused by air and brine, all our senses, including sight, hearing and smell, have a much higher sensitivity.

Through electromagnetic technology, we have some sense of a finer world, simply in the way we can transmit music and pictures with such perfection to any part of the universe. And certain echoes of other worlds are now coming into modern physics. A 5-dimensional world would seem to solve some of the problems of General Relativity. In *Mind, Body and Electromagnetism*, I conjectured about a 6-dimensional duality, three of space and three of time. Today, our *String* theorists operate in an 11-dimensional world, 4 of normal space-time, and 7 that are closed to human perception. With this formulation, they envisage numberless invisible universes which interact and sustain our system. The *Big-Bang*, and the cosmic background radiation, are seen as evidence for such a theory.

Mystics and adepts all seem to agree that the higher planes are *substantial*. Space and time are much as we experience them here, with bodies and plants and buildings of much finer and indestructible material. Education, scientific research, literature, music, painting, architecture continue to be developed, but at levels relevant to the changed conditions of existence. Visitations are made from higher to lower planes, and so it is reasonable that Myers would have indirect knowledge of regions that he hadn't yet graduated to. However, many wonder what the real motive for life could be, given that the external conditions are seemingly devoid of the strife and conflict experienced on earth. Some suggest we spend much of our time trying to correct for earthly misdeeds and unkindnesses; but that sounds implausible in the long term. Once these are clearly recognised and understood, surely we can move on.

As for Church doctrine and dogma, one gets the impression that they count for little, and often become a barrier to simple truths. We build up our spiritual account on this earth through openness and natural kindness to others, and this alone determines our initial status in the higher domains. The spiritual or sacramental path in this life may help indirectly; but if it leads to narrow and judgmental attitudes, it has no value. Such a view is of course quite unacceptable to many orthodox Christians. However, to be fair to the Anglican Church, they do have at least have a serious research group in their *Fellowship for Psychical and Spiritual Studies.*

We should take into account, as Myers often suggests, that there are likely to be major language problems in all of this. Even on our own terrestrial level, it is hardly possible to describe colour to the blind, or music to the deaf. Scientists often give up on normal language to express new concepts, and much is now expressed only in mathematics, which is unintelligible to most of the human race. Similarly, Indian philosophers point out the problems caused by our attempts to translate into English certain Sanskrit words expressing complex concepts and processes.

To take these ideas seriously, imagination must play an important part. It does of course play a vital part in all our lives, for nothing is achieved, even in the most rigorous sciences, without it. There are many like myself who, after a religious childhood, look for some new spiritual direction. The concept of a God looking after us, protecting us from wars and natural disasters and illnesses and accidents through a certain type of religious obedience, has not proved meaningful or helpful. In some ways, when disaster strikes, we are more vulnerable than those without belief.

The message coming through Geraldine Cummins puts everything in a much wider context. It is comforting and helpful. It is a worthy conception, in which we see the various stages of our life here reflected in similar stages in the wider cosmic pattern. Death is not a great tragedy, but part of the natural evolution of life. There is freedom to move on, to move back, to commune with those we love, to develop new interests, to review past experience. It is a positive view, one that strengthens us in the daily struggle of life on this earth. I think it implies that earth-life is the most challenging of all; and how we cope with the difficulties, rather than any success, is ultimately what matters. It is certainly worth thinking about.

In my own experience and reading, it is the communications that come through hypnosis and automatic writing that are the most fascinating, and worthy of study. Many of the popular methods of communication through intermediaries and mediums have little to commend them, for much of the material is trivial, and there are few suggestions of the broader picture of life that Myers is trying to get across. Certainly this became the experience of the members of the Society for Psychical Research.

Jane Sherwood is an interesting case. She lost her husband in World War I, and tried to get in contact with him through conventional spiritualist methods. For her, this turned out to be a rather depressing and frustrating experience. So instead she experimented with automatic writing, and eventually acquired her own communicators who brought her into contact with her husband.

Her book, *The Psychic Bridge*, containing much philosophical and scientific material, can be said to throw new light on many matters. The following passage from one of her communicators rather wonderfully turns the whole Darwinian argument on its head, or inside out, and will make eminent sense to many thinking people.

'Species that took the path of specialisation in self-defensive

devices, or in ferocity, branched off from the road and took the cul-de-sac of specialised form and habits which were proof and cause of their failure. If their biological devices for self-protection succeeded, their armour became their grave. They paid for safety by loss of power to feel and by corresponding loss of awareness and intelligence. Life always measures success by its highest emergent value, and when that value became intelligence, it began to discard the forms which specialised in the lower qualities. The emergence and pre-eminence of the human species with its absence of defensive biological devices was in contrast to this. Man had refused the physical adaptation calculated to give safety and had followed the lines of an ascending quality of life. He had demanded of life that it should give more and not less of feeling, emotion, perception, passion, beauty. That this development was self-imposed by life, a production of its line of advance towards more fullness of life was proved by its continuance in other forms of being, by the lifting of human life and values on to other planes by the very intensity of the life force thus engendered.

It was true that the deathward tendency was always to be seen contending with life. Too often individuals and nations took the cul-de-sac, refused suffering, made themselves strong in force and ferocity, sold their birthright of suffering for dangerous safety and power. Yet every empire founded in force and embodying ideals which were treacherous to the special quality of human life was denied of life and came to ruin. All that survived from each of such colossal follies were the elements of virtue of which it had remained faithful to life. Babylon, Egypt, Greece, and Rome rolled up their great empires. But the wisdom of Egypt, the art of Greece, the law of Rome remained to enrich the races that followed. The human story endorsed the dictum that love is the fulfilling of the law, and the cumulative effects of the working of this law were written plainly in the story of men and of nations.'

Deep down, most of us hope that the meek will, one day, inherit the earth.

When I was young, I found it difficult to understand what I was doing in this strange and puzzling world, where everything seemed so troublesome and difficult. Having no natural desire to compete for anything, this was a very alien place. I was continuously appalled by the cruelty, with educated leaders considering themselves heroes after slaughtering innocent civilians. My general conclusion has been that if there were not gentler conditions of existence somewhere in the universe, then better not to have anything at all. However, having gone through the major trials of life, I am beginning to think that the earth experience has something rather special about it. To survive with one's soul intact, having only minimally compromised with the darker forces, is a good feeling. The heroism of those who stick to their beliefs and values in the face of continuous abuse and ridicule is warming. And the beauty there is, existing in such adverse conditions, is all the more remarkable.

Spiritualists, rightly or wrongly, have taken a rather heroic stand. They have stated the case for something gentler, something nearer the heart's desire. And in helping to keep alive the notion of the soul, the independence of the soul, they have helped to keep alive a concept of mental freedom, without which there can be no meaningful science, and no civilised world.

As for scientists, what we can deduce from all the above is that those who have taken just a cursory interest in psychical research find nothing of value. Those who were prepared to put serious time and effort into it found evidence that was compelling.

Chapter Nine

Some Personal Recollections

I have little desire to explain my life or specific actions. Such an exercise generally results in forms of self-justification, with considerable unfairness to other people. But coming towards the later stages of one's life, there may be some usefulness in discussing ideas, impressions, feelings, and the complex intangibles that cause us to adopt certain attitudes in the living of a thoughtful life. Why one person inclines towards Christianity or atheism, socialism or capitalism, mysticism or monism, is generally of interest. Everyone's life has something to teach us, whether or not they have the time or inclination or specialist knowledge to take part in the great debates on the great issues.

What follows are odd events, odd thoughts of my life that have some connection, often vague and distant, with the writing of this book. Hopefully, these fragments of personal memories may help to fill out for the reader a picture provided by the remainder of this book. I cannot point to any stage of my life where there was a radical conversion to a new way of thinking, to a philosophy or a religion. Rather certain general attitudes were formed in childhood, to be followed by a steady working-out of the details. I have not been a joiner of movements, rather an agnostic who views from a distance. I could seldom convince myself that one particular group had so much more to offer than others.

This is not to suggest a life lacking enthusiasms. For the first half of it, various forms of music and sport occupied much of my time, as it did with most of the family circle. All this provided formative experiences, not just in developing some particular skill, but in terms of friendship, responsibility, and working with people from a variety of backgrounds.

But enthusiasm for belief systems was always a problem. Sometimes I was a rather envious of those who had great conviction about what they were doing, whether in science or religion, and wondered about the origin of such confidence. How did people, with totally opposite views, come to be so sure within themselves? Was this wisdom, or delusion, or just a tactic for gaining power? There seemed to be no simple answers. The thought processes of each one of us are so infinitely complex.

With music, there was always a sense of mystery in that I could never quite rationalise what was going on in my mind, and why musical vibrations had such an effect on me. When performing for others, I was sometimes able to watch, in a quite detached way, this wonderful process from mind and memory to muscle movement. What does it mean to watch oneself doing something? Who is watching whom?

Although a demanding discipline, music has been the most enjoyable part of life. And when playing with or accompanying others, all anxiety and nervousness disappears. Happily there was never anything competitive, and the idea of continually proving myself better than others has never appealed. I do in fact love to hear pianists who have mastered things I have never mastered, and can appreciate the sacrifices necessary to reach the highest standards. But that sort of dedication inevitably limits what can be done with other talents.

That said, I realise that not having to be competitive is a privilege, and not the norm. In most areas of life, particularly in earning a living, it is extremely difficult to avoid the competitive element. Making a judgement as to how far to compete against others to protect an existing position, or gain a new position, is one of the greatest challenges in life. In this we show our deepest values. To retain these, it is sometimes necessary to take the greatest risks - for ourselves and our families and dependants. And having taken the risk, and failed in a worldly sense, there may be no comfort from those we love and respect. It can either be the beginning of a real stage of inner growth, or of depression and despair.

The love of music is intimately bound up with religious ideas, for much of the greatest music has a religious character. Music, together with art and sculpture and architecture, evolved mainly through religious ritual. So many great musicians have developed their skills through the church, and so many of the greatest works have a religious theme. However, although religious thought focuses on all those very desirable qualities of life, of kindness, thoughtfulness, openness, honesty, generosity, the specific belief systems tend to reinforce my agnosticism. While taking an interest in different ways of expressing belief, and different cultural traditions, I have found it quite impossible to accept absolute claims. If we have to choose, it must be what we are most comfortable with rather than any dogmatic statement of belief.

This agnosticism applies very much to scientific ideas. Throughout my life, I have seen many supposedly incontrovertible facts and theories come and go. As an undergraduate, a theory of continuous creation was all the rage. In my middle years, the universe came into existence fourteen billion years ago, and cosmologists worked out the details down to the first thousandth of a second. A few years ago I read in *Nature* that not too many top people now accept this. For most of the twentieth century, Quantum Mechanics was of the essence. Now the very best physicists say that no one really understands it any more. The constancy of the velocity of light is at the heart of Relativity; but recent research suggests that it automatically adjusts itself to the geometry of space-time.

There is no basic issue about science moving on from one theoretical formulation to another. But there is a serious issue if temporary theories and conjectures are put across as essential truths. There is an increasing dogmatism at the heart of science, of similar nature to theological doctrine and belief. Those who engage wholeheartedly in the current orthodoxy get the research grants, the prizes, and the professorships. And when they apply their assumptions to practical problems in medicine and agriculture, they can endanger the whole health of our society.

For such reasons, we seriously need agnosticism. We need to stand back and view the wider consequences. We need it most of all in the psychological and genetic areas where there exists the greatest dogmatism, and the most dangerous assumptions. Here a very serious scepticism is required. Those who make all sorts of improbable assumptions about the brain and thought and consciousness, and refuse absolutely to consider quite different but reasonable viewpoints about the nature of mental activity, should be seriously challenged. So often today, on television programs about natural healing or organic farming for instance, are we forced to listen to some "rational" commentator who proposes something far less plausible than the alternative and supposedly irrational view.

It is of course difficult to make any worthwhile impact without going through the Western educational disciplines, and absorbing the main material of the physical and life sciences. My own life has been a privileged one compared with the vast majority of people in this world, with the opportunity to study the physical sciences in my youth, then to be involved in technology and software for many years, and later in the biological sciences. My judgements may be wrong and misguided; but I think it would be wasteful of life's experiences not to try to make them.

My early years, in which most of my general attitudes were formed, I look back on with considerable pleasure. I was the youngest of three children, and the family was strong and secure. My sister was three years older, and brother six years. We lived in a lovely village about twenty-five miles north-east of London. My parents were relatively poor; but in our school years, there was no lack of opportunities because of this. My brother and I went to the local grammar school, my sister had some secretarial training, and we all had music lessons. By today's standards, life was strict, but also reasonably fair, and definitely very full.

My mother came from a very caring non-conformist family, and was generous beyond her means. Anyone who came to the door - and there were many tramps passing through the village in the 1930s - were made welcome and generally fed. Her parents were strong members of the Salvation Army in their earlier years. My father was not so fortunate with his family, being the son of an exceptionally strict village headmaster.

At fourteen, he ran away with an elder brother to the army, and after a two-year spell came back to the village to become apprenticed to a carpenter. Then he had a second army spell in the Tank Corps in World War I when he was injured, but not too seriously. His rather severe disposition gradually mellowed over the years as he drew closer to my mother's family, many of whom lived in the village. He even changed his Sunday ritual, moving from the Anglican Church to the Congregational Chapel to which my mother and her relations were so devoted. Late on in life after my mother had died, he did some of his best work for the chapel organ and pulpit.

Religion was a serious matter for us, and played a major part in all our lives. Fortunately there was no established doctrine that I was expected to adhere to. The Congregational Church was probably the most democratic religious institution in the country, and each minister and congregation had the freedom to pursue their spiritual quest as they chose. I remember there was one church in London where the minister took his whole congregation into the Catholic Church. Later in life, when visiting New England, I came to realise what a powerful influence this church had been, and still is, in the development of the United States. Attending services at Harvard University and in central Boston in my fifties took me right back to childhood days.

Sunday was a very special day, a day different from all others. Everyone put on their best clothes, and behaved and spoke rather more gently than usual. There was Sunday School, morning and evening services, and an afternoon Anglican service during the war that I played the organ for. The ritual of my Sunday in the 1930s included a shortish village walk before midday dinner, a long walk of about six miles through fields in the afternoon, and an hour's walk in the summer evenings. Later in the evening, there was always music and hymns around the piano or harmonium. Someone once gave us some *six-hand* music, and with myself at the bottom, my sister in the middle, and brother in the top, and we were rather proud of ourselves when we managed to finish together.

Many of my contemporaries resented their Sunday religious ritual;

and had I been brought up in strict Catholic or Anglican traditions, dutifully reciting things I had no natural inclination to believe, bewailing my miserable sins, and suggesting to God that He keeps His promises, I would probably have wished to opt out. But overall, I look back on those childhood Sundays as kindly and cleansing days, with a distinctive change of consciousness. Some sermons might have been boring; but many were quite memorable. I never found such reasonable beliefs and convictions in other churches and societies, even in the Society of Friends. As for the oratorical skills, sadly they hardly seem to exist today.

Both parents had ambitions for their children seemingly much beyond those of other working-class parents in the village. The pressure to do well and to please was always present, and I suppose modern fashionable opinion would think this not too healthy. I avoided any such pressure with my own children, but am not convinced that was necessarily a good thing. Sometimes I disappointed my father or my teachers, and that could be difficult. But coping with such difficulties is probably an important aspect of growing up.

Much of the detail of childhood slips away from the memory. But two things predominate, even over music and sport. One was the countryside, and the other was the war - World War II. For any child not to be brought up in natural countryside (intense farming is very unnatural) is, to me, a great disadvantage. Fortunately for my own three daughters, they were close to farms and fields in their early years. For my son, the best we could manage was a house right on the edge of Cambridge. But none of them had the freedom of the children in my village. Long summer days in the woods and fields and our special trees, searching for birds' nests or picking blackberries, cricket and football until we dropped - innocent pleasures unspoilt by parental fears about our absence for a few hours. Many of the fields were pasture before the war, most full of rabbits, and only the occasional farmer tried to keep out the public. There was so much to explore, so much to be interested in, so much mystery and magic never to be found in a laboratory.

The war gave us even more freedom to roam. My father, like so many others, often worked twelve hours a day, seven days a week in a factory for much of the war, not to mention frequent fire duty for the whole night. Children were expected to entertain themselves and not bother grown-ups unnecessarily. However there were extra responsibilities, not least of which was the growing of vegetables to last the whole winter. This took up a considerable amount of time in the spring and late summer, particularly after my brother had left home for the RAF. But the importance of such work was always understood, given the very severe rationing of food and the obvious difficulties of all mothers in finding enough to put on the table.

My secondary education coincided with the war years. From the declaration of war, life changed dramatically for all of us. On that fateful Sunday morning at the chapel morning service, the minister kept leaving the pulpit and going back to the Manse next door. Then he announced what Chamberlain had said on the radio, and very shortly after there was an air raid warning. We all rushed home, began putting mattresses against the window, and attempted to seal the windows from gas attack - about which we had heard much, and were very fearful of. There was considerable commotion out in the street, with a retired colonel, a massive man, ordering people about and generally stirring things up. My father, in what to me was his bravest moment, told him to calm down and go home, and actually physically pushed him away. All of that happened within an hour of the war declaration.

The village, being in the path of enemy bombers from the Low Countries, had a very noisy war, with lots of anti-aircraft batteries in the vicinity. There were also curious searchlight installations out in the fields nearby which heightened the excitement or fear. Many bombs were jettisoned in the surrounding countryside, aircraft crashed nearby, a cluster of incendiaries fell on the village, and a landmine (a very large bomb on the end of a parachute) exploded in the churchyard seriously damaging the church and blowing out our front windows and our back door. In the earlier years of the war, we either sheltered under the kitchen table or in the cupboard under the stairs. Later, we had considerable fun trying to construct two shelters in the garden, one of which was generally water-logged, and the other plagued with insects.

For young people, the Battle of Britain was the most spectacular event, some of it taking place right over the village. People stood in the sun, and cheered when a plane was shot down, hopefully assuming it was not one of ours. The most disturbing time for all of us was near the end of the war when the pilotless V-1 doodlebugs were droning away morning, noon, and night, and one's instinct was to hope that the engine would keep going and land somewhere else. Up to that point, we had become somehow immune to normal bombing raids. But there was real terror in this.

How barbaric is this business of bombing innocent people. I well remember my horror as a young boy in the 1930s seeing newsreel pictures of the bombing of Chinese cities by the Japanese. When the Germans bombed Rotterdam early in World War II, and thousands were killed in a few hours, there was total revulsion in this country. But eventually, after some of our own cities had been seriously damaged, we all became criminals, cheering on the destruction of German and Japanese cities. At the end, we were able to wipe out a city in a few seconds. Sadly, even today, our politicians seem to have few qualms doing similar things to innocent Serbs and Iraqis. It is, incredibly, sometimes referred to in the press as "humanitarian bombing".

At school, the war continued during the morning hours. It seems that the Luftwaffe put their feet up in the afternoon because I never remember games being disturbed by air raids. But for the first two years of the war, we spent long morning hours in the shelters, doing absolutely nothing. Sometimes there was no time to get to the shelters, and we just disappeared under the desks. How we longed for the sirens to go when a physics test was pending!

I often think about that strange cold sensation when first entering a physics laboratory at the age of ten. Was it created by the very strict teacher, or the subject, or both? When reaching the sixth form level, I pleaded to be allowed to study maths and languages, never physics and chemistry. But to no avail. One had to join exclusively either the sciences or arts. Fortunately a superb chemistry teacher came back from the war, and that subject quickly began to make some definite sense. But throughout my school years, physics remained a curious arbitrary business, full of artificial conventions that seemed to come out of nowhere.

For my first five years at the school, there was an elderly mathematics master, a Mr Ross, who had been persuaded to keep going beyond retirement during the war years. To me, he was rather special, somehow standing out from the rest. Small in stature, a gentle man, loath to give punishment, he had a difficult time with some of the boys, but never lost his cool. I heard that he had studied both mathematics and history at university; and there were strange rumours that he was a Buddhist. He took part in all the school activities, producing plays, umpiring matches, attending all the concerts. He sometimes stood in for other teachers, and we would all have learned a great deal more about literature and science in his knowledgeable hands.

From him I had my first introduction to the basics of Euclidean geometry, and that was the most unforgettable part of my education. Presenting this elegant system of thought, of which I had no previous awareness, with such beautifully-drawn pictures of circles and lines, was truly memorable. Later, at the university, I came to love the even more remarkable system of Projective Geometry which grew out of Euclidean concepts. After graduating, I had the pleasure to present for a few years the Euclidean system to hundreds of pupils, and the Projective system to a handful of gifted young mathematicians. Soon after leaving teaching, these beautiful thought-forms were largely eliminated from both schools and universities by a new breed of educationalists who considered the formal logic of geometry unsuitable for the modern age.

When I was thirteen, the school went out of its way to find me a semi-professional pianist under which to study for a few years. Every Thursday afternoon I would cycle about three miles to another lovely village, and partly along a footpath through the fields. Curiously in my memory, it was always summer, although the schedule continued summer

157

and winter for five years. There by the village green was this charming old timber-fronted house. After knocking at the imposing door and being let in by one of the maids, I entered a quite different world - one of considerable sophistication and taste that was so different from my normal life. The maid would lead me into the Library, and then bring me a large tray of tea and bread and cakes. After what was to me a substantial meal, I made my way to the elegant drawing room with a grand piano once belonging to Clifford Curzon, my teacher's teacher.

Eventually, about an hour after my arrival, Mrs Hales made her entrance, generally with her large wolfhound that had definite likes and dislikes in music. She was probably in her fifties, married to an inspector of schools, and elegant in an upper middle-class way. Her sons went to a top independent school; and when she referred to "Exhibitions at Cambridge", it was quite some time before I knew what she was talking about (an Exhibition being a form of minor scholarship to a Cambridge College). She had not made the highest grade in piano playing, but worked very seriously at it for her entire life. Her recitals during the war were highly regarded by the Chelmsford musical fraternity.

In her piano teaching, she had just a few pupils who were self-motivated, and charged my parents a modest sum of about two guineas per term. Lessons continued until she felt no more could be done, sometimes lasting up to two hours. All her other pupils were female. With me, she had the task of removing some terrible playing habits, and, in her terms, of civilising me generally. One day when I took liberties with a Chopin impromptu, she pleaded with me never to say she was my teacher if that is what I wanted to do. One had to understand the difference between sentiment and sentimentality.

This was a musical education of a sort, a very specialist one focusing entirely on the basic piano repertoire of Beethoven, Chopin, Schumann, and a few others. School provided a more general musical education, having to play with the orchestra and in ensembles. All my earlier lessons had been in my own village with a cousin of my mother who was largely self-taught. For the last two or three years with Mrs Harrington, we spent the time mainly sight-reading many of Haydn's symphonies arranged for four hands. A certain love and admiration of Haydn, and rather marginal interest in Mozart, remained with me for much of my life - partly related to his rather uninspiring piano sonatas, and partly to the predictability of his music. Haydn was a modest man, always underestimating his own abilities. In general, I prefer composers who had to work hard at expressing their ideas. Brahms took seventeen years composing his first symphony, and it was worth it. The emergence of Mozart as *the* composer, and his operas as deep psychological statements, would seem very strange to the musical tutors of my youth. However, after my youngest daughter took me to see the film *Amadeus*, I began to wonder if I was missing out on something. Later, I saw the film twice in Madrid, and watched people coming out of the cinema emotionally drained and in tears.

Surprising to look back on were the occasional visits to London after school to attend the Promenade Concerts at the Royal Albert Hall. The war was on, there were often air raids, and yet my mother gave me the freedom to make this journey, arriving back about midnight. Only during the worst stages of the V-1 assault were the public concerts cancelled - although they continued to be broadcast from a BBC studio. One enduring memory was the sight of Sir Henry Wood in magnificent white suit conducting Tschaikowsky's fifth symphony just a little way above my arena position. This may have been his last concert because a few days later he died. Those were wonderful occasions during the war, and everyone so friendly. One composer new to me that greatly impressed was Granville Bantock - so seldom played today. While happy to see that the Proms are still flourishing, I continue to be amazed that English people are still so subservient to authority that they consent to stand in the arena for a two-and-a-half hour concert.

The RAF years I look back on with a little nostalgia. The first ten weeks were terrible, probably much worse than prison. Up in the morning about six o-clock, parades, drill, inspections, fatigues, battle-courses, bayonet drill, tin-room duties in the cookhouse, endless cleaning of buttons and boots, all taking place in an atmosphere of iron discipline. I was once given a long dressing-down in front of all the rest for a small cake that had been found behind my pillow. We soon came to realise what it takes to get and control an Empire. But of course there is a certain camaraderie that develops, and people help each other through. Nevertheless, suicide was a relatively common occurrence which seemed not to worry the authorities.

After this everything eased. I received some intelligent training as a wireless mechanic, learning more about electricity, magnetism, and radio technology in a few weeks than I had done in seven years at school. All of which was reinforced in a practical way by eighteen months of installing new systems around the country. Making my own low-frequency oscillators thirty years later was a rather simple matter.

The two years in the RAF were followed by three years at Cambridge studying mathematics. Not taking part in a single concert during all this time represented a significant change of life. There was some music in the RAF, when I occasionally played on an old NAAFI piano. But a place like Cambridge, seething with would-be professional musicians so anxious to display their talents, is certainly no place for the uncompetitive. There was of course plenty to listen to in the college chapels, and choral evensong at Kings eventually became something I seldom missed. That was all new to me, as were the great choral and organ works of Bach.

By the time we got to university, we were no longer boys, and the academic enthusiasm of school was gone. The average age of undergraduates was then about twenty-five, many having served in the navy during the war. We were advised to attend lectures in the morning, do something sporting in the afternoon, work a little between afternoon tea and dinner, and enjoy the societies in the evening. The only constraint was a weekly meeting with our tutor with some work. Most of my friends were on the arts side, and from whom I learnt much.

My own tutor, the college chaplain, had read both mathematics and theology. Unmarried, a lifetime's devotion to the college, knowledgeable in many subjects, he was keen for his pupils to accept his own High Anglican version of Christianity. But we could never really get to know much about him, or other fellows, largely because of one curious obstacle: direct questions were regarded as discourteous. Apparently Samuel Johnson once said that 'a gentleman's conversation doth not consist of asking questions', and that was pointed out to all new undergraduates. Maybe this was a defensive mechanism; but my little experience of the Senior Common Room inclines me to think that this attitude has stunted intellectual conversation at high table for generations. I so much prefer the attitude of American academics who, if you have anything new to say, bombard you with questions. It was through an open-minded American professor of zoology, David Deamer, that I began the serious study of the life sciences later in life. Cambridge academics would do better to follow Socrates and Plato rather than Samuel Johnson.

I chose to study maths, partly out of natural interest, and partly because I knew that if I didn't learn it then, it was unlikely I would ever do so. With a mathematical background, most other science-based subjects can be picked up through general reading. There was also a curiosity about the strange entity called the Maths Tripos - I was aware of George Bernard Shaw's play, *Mrs Warren's Profession*, in which the daughter was being given a respectable life from the mother's immoral earnings by going to Cambridge and taking the Tripos - so called because students once graduated by arguing with an examiner sitting on a three-legged stool.

While quite a lot of the maths was of little interest, the pure knowledge of Projective Geometry, almost unique to Cambridge, was a privilege to learn; and Electromagnetics, taught by Hermann Bondi, was equally fascinating. Sadly, as previously indicated, the former is not taught any more, while the latter is hurriedly covered in current undergraduate courses. To my way of thinking, these thought-forms are crowning achievements of the human mind, combining the highest levels of perception, intuition, and rationality. The fact that Rudolf Steiner often commented on the power of Projective Geometry, and encouraged its study in his own Steiner and Waldorf schools, was certainly a reason for my devoting about eighteen months to the study of his extensive writings. He felt this was the best analytical method for understanding the geometry of living forms.

Music came back into my life when I took a post in Londonderry, Northern Ireland. Although officially a maths teacher, it was here that I gained my real musical education. In my first year, I took serious organ lessons with the cathedral organist, Dr Michael Franklin, and worked through some of the Bach repertoire. There is of course a huge difference between playing a one-manual village organ with a small pedal board and a few stops, and a large four-manual instrument with an almost infinite variety of registration. Michael was much older than I, rather a large man for an organist, entirely without conceit, and often in trouble with the Dean who had definite musical views. He gave me lessons in harmony and counterpoint, and always invited me to do the piano accompaniments for visiting singers. When sufficiently competent on the organ, I became his official assistant. We studied together many of the major choral works, working through the full score and adapting parts to the organ. This was a lovely time, probably the best of my life. From him, I learnt for the first time how music was actually put together, and this is so much more rewarding than the repetitive discipline for performing particular pieces.

As for Londonderry itself, I loved the beautiful blue hills that surrounded us, the magnificent river Foyle, the Inishowen Peninsula between the Foyle and the even more magnificent Swilly, and perhaps above all, the unique beauty and wildness of the Donegal mountains. The people, both Protestant and Catholic, were friendly and generous, and their natural talent for music most appealing. The political situation then was reasonably stable, and improving. A few thought that my walking through the Bogside each morning to work was very dangerous, and others considered that playing soccer, or dealing with the Catholic travel agency, was letting the side down a little. But these were small matters; and I noted how Protestant colleagues loved their holidays in the south, or the weekend trip to the metropolis in Dublin. Many institutions were organised on an all-Ireland basis, and I took part in concerts on both sides of the border. However, the long military struggle over the last three decades has destroyed the optimism of the 1950s, and darker forces have taken over. Sadly, Ireland loses so many of its best young people to other countries without the ethnic problems.

After four years in Londonderry, I returned to England, to a less friendly world, and continued to earn a living teaching maths and giving much of my spare time to local concerts. Part of my teaching was at a Quaker School (Society of Friends), and in taking the post, there was a thought that maybe I would find a way of life more in tune with my beliefs and feelings. It began well, and I made a few friends for life - perhaps the best that anyone could ask. I have always supported the peace-makers, but could not give an unequivocal commitment to pacifism. In the working-out of this idea in a school environment, I wondered if a little physical violence might even be preferable to certain strict judgmental attitudes that can be a form of violence. The explicit non-ritual of their services appealed only for a short while, for one was totally at the mercy of all the individual prejudices around. Ritual is not only a comfort, but protects us from a certain form of exploitation.

After the age of thirty, the prospect of going through a similar annual routine until retirement became a little depressing, and there was a need for a new stimulus and challenge. Surprisingly, after failing to get something in the musical world, I was offered a post as a systems analyst in a computers and automation company, in spite of my age and zero experience. They obviously found it difficult to get any sort of mathematician into the newly developing computerised world of process-control.

This field of work outside music and teaching, and without rules or precedents or standards, quickly proved rather attractive. Although viewed with considerable suspicion early on by bright young engineers, I found the business of trying to solve quite new problems extremely invigorating. Fortunately I was immediately involved with one of best process-control projects around at that time, in which British and American firms would try to develop an on-line information system for a new oil refinery. The most basic task was to work out a way of monitoring about fifteen hundred instruments, most of them every two minutes. We had also to devise software for scheduling the refinery operations, from crude oil tankers coming in, through distillation and blending, and to the export of the final products.

These were pioneering days when one began from an empty machine with no standardised operating systems or diagnostic procedures. When we were in serious difficulties with very low-level problems, we sometimes had to step through thousands of lines of machine-code programming, reading the octal-number lights on a console. The mental effort of doing this over many days and nights for a single critical problem, and for many months prior to the final tests, was immense - quite the most intense intellectual exercise of my life. Taking all that into account, the total project time to completion of about five years was very reasonable.

After eighteen months, the software was subcontracted to a company I was allowed to form, and suddenly I found myself being referred to as an entrepreneur - a term that meant what it said in those days. I became a between-taker, albeit approved of by the two major companies. Many years were to follow in entrepreneurial software, involving new computer languages, graphical systems, mathematical libraries, structural engineering, and remaining a challenge throughout.

Now computers are supposed to be the most materialistic of things, and one might expect hard-line scientific attitudes to pervade throughout. But, as already indicated, this has not been my experience. In fact, among engineers generally, there is far more openness about new ideas than in academic science. This has to be so. In technology, one has to solve specific practical problems - not roughly solve them, but absolutely so. Anyone with novel ideas based on real knowledge and experience can contribute. In academic studies, just the top few people in any speciality decide the approach that is to be taken for the next few years. It is sometimes necessary to wait for a generation of top scientists to die off before a new approach can be adopted.

Computer software gave me the first significant thoughts about complex systems, and how they might be built up. Not much complexity is required to discover that, for any sort of flexibility or ruggedness or reliability, the system must be organised into relatively small modular units that perform specific tasks. As the system develops, one builds in various levels of hierarchical control. This is what happens in our own bodies. The cells are the fundamental units, particularly the germ cells. These form tissues, then organs, then systems of blood and nerve to control the organs, then brain and hormone centres to control the systems. Unless you adopt this approach with software, you will get into a terrible mess. Only with modular structures can a complex system be sensibly constructed and developed.

Eventually I gained some limited freedom from my work to explore more generally such thoughts. The Cambridge University Library, probably the world's greatest library in that so much is available on the open shelves, provided the opportunity to study subjects not easily accessible in any other way. Orthodox and unorthodox, Western and Eastern literature about the human systems, became my food and drink for many years. This brought back intuitions from my university years when I was led into new fields of thought in geometry and electromagnetics. The possibility of a some quite new theorising about human structure, or morphogenesis, involving electromagnetic, musical, geometrical, and software concepts slowly began to make some sense to me; and after about twelve years, the first edition of *Mind, Body and Electromagnetism* emerged.

As we have seen in this book, current research is giving considerable credence to such ideas. There are varied studies into the effects of oscillating electrical fields on cell membranes and chicken embryos; geomagnetic field rhythms relate to brain rhythms and the growth of living systems; magnetic resonance scanners are observing the deeper workings of the brain and body; low-frequency oscillators are being used in medicine for wound and bone healing and pain control; man-made fields have strong correlations with cancerous conditions, particularly leukemia. One of the most promising developments for me over the last five years is the explosive new interest in biological mathematics, and extensive use of engineering methods to model aspects of the body. Some of this was hinted at optimistically in the previous book, but the actual movement in this direction is beyond all expectation.

The cooperative work of biologists, physicists, mathematicians, and doctors should have far-reaching implications for the future direction of medicine. Among many thinking people, there is a realisation that the highly invasive techniques of modern surgery, the chemical therapies that damage the immune system, and the possibly even more damaging genetic techniques currently being contemplated, are not sensible ways to achieve what we want to achieve. Our natural processes depend on the correct functioning of the electrical systems of nerves, muscles, and in fact of all types of cells. This is a level that we can influence without difficulty with modern electronic, electrical, and electromagnetic methods - at any current level, at any field strength, at any frequency, and with any pulse shape. This I hope will be a major scientific project for the new century.

A new focus in physics research should assist these developments. During the last century, with the help of quantum mechanics, physicists concentrated their attention on unseen high-frequency radiations, from radio waves to infra-red, from ultra-violet to gamma rays. During the coming century, it looks as though interest will change to the other end of the spectrum - to the extremely low frequency vibrations of the whole earth and its surrounding ionosphere, and that relate to fundamental frequencies in living systems. Science is just beginning to confirm the Indian concept of a *silent sound* that creates and sustains all life.

Most of us will never know whether or not we have done anything useful. We live in hope; and the best we can do is to persevere. There is certainly a moral duty to challenge if we seriously feel that something is leading us in wrong and dangerous directions. If our challenge is unsuccessful, we will at least have tried. Just in the process of trying, we will discover new things, and meet others who can broaden our outlook. Whatever, best not to take ourselves too seriously, and best to allow for worldly failure. But failure is often just a temporary matter. The cosmos is teeming with ideas, circulating through billions of minds. If our knowledge is accompanied by open-mindedness, there is always a chance of finding a better way. If there is generosity as well, we leave something memorable behind for our friends.

Selected Reading

Attenborough, David, *Life on Earth*,
Collins, 1979.
Balinsky, B.I., *An Introduction to Embryology*,
W B Saunders, 1965.
Barrett, William, *Death of the Soul*,
Oxford University Press, 1986.
Becker, Robert O and Marino, Andrew A, *Electromagnetism and Life*, State University of New York Press, 1982.
Blavatsky, H P, *The Mahatma Letters*,
Theosophical Publishing Society, 1910.
Borgia, Anthony, *Life in the World Unseen*,
Psychic Press, 1954.
Bouquet, A C, *Comparative Religion*,
Penguin Books, 1956.
Bowler, Peter J, *Evolution. The History of an Idea*,
University of California Press, 1982.
Burkhardt, Richard W, *The Spirit of System. Lamarck and Evolutionary Biology*, Harvard University Press, 1977.
Buranelli, Vincent, *The Wizard from Vienna*,
Peter Owen, 1976.
Cannon, Graham H, *Lamarck and Modern Genetics*,
Manchester University Press, 1959.
Castillejo, David, *The Expanding Force in Newton's Cosmos*,
Ediciones de Arte y Bibliofilia, Madrid, 1981.
Cerminara, Gina, *Many Mansions*,
Neville Spearman, 1967.
Changeux, Jean-Pierre, *Neuronal Man*,
Oxford University Press, 1985.
Child, C M, *Patterns and Problems of Development*,
Chicago University Press, 1941.
Clark, Ronald W, *The Survival of Charles Darwin*,

Random House, 1984.

Cohen, David, *Magnetic Fields of the human body*,
  Physics Today, 1975.

Cummins, Geraldine, *The Road to Immortality*,
  Psychic Press, 1932.

Davies, P V W, Brown J (editors),
  Superstrings: A Theory of Everything?,
  Cambridge University Press, 1988.

Darwin, Charles,
  The Origin of Species, John Murray, 1906.
  The Descent of Man, Princeton University Press, 1981.

Deamer, David W, *Being Human*,
  Saunders College Publishing, 1981.

Dirac, Paul, *Directions in Physics*,
  John Wiley & Sons, 1978.

Dubrov, A P, *The Geomagnetic Field and Life*,
  Plenum Press, 1978.

Eccles, John C, *The Understanding of the Brain*,
  McGraw-Hill, 1977.

Einstein, Albert, *Ideas and Opinions*,
  Souvenir Press, 1973.

Eisendrath, Craig, *The Unifying Moment*,
  Harvard University Press, 1971.

Evans, John, *Mind, Body and Electromagnetism*,
  Ross-Evans, 1992.

Garrett, Eileen, *My Life as a Search for the Meaning of
  Mediumship*,   Rider & Co., 1939.

Gasman, Daniel, *The Scientific Origins of National Socialism*,
  Macdonald & Co., 1971.

Haeckel, Ernst, *The Riddle of the Universe*,
  Watts & Co., 1900.

Harwood, A C, *The Faithful Thinker*,
  Hodder and Stoughton, 1961.

Heisenberg, Werner, *Physics and Beyond*,
  George Allen & Unwin, 1971.

Iverson, Jeffrey, *More Lives than One*,
  Sourvenir Press, 1976.

James, William,
  The Principles of Psychology, Dover Publications, 1950;
  A Pluralistic Universe, Harvard University Press, 1977;
  Psychical Research, Chatto & Windus, 1961.
Jenny, Hans, *Cymatics*,
  Basilius Press, 1966.
Jung, C G, *Modern Man in Search of a Soul*,
  Routledge & Kegan Paul, 1978.
Koestler, Arthur, *Janus: A Summing Up*,
  Pan Books, 1979.
Lashley, K S, *The Neuro-Psychology of Lashley: Selected Papers*,
  McGraw-Hill, 1960.
Liu, Astumian, and Tsong, *Activation of Na+ and K+ Pumping
  Modes by an Oscillating Electric Field*,
  Journal of Biological Chemistry, May, 1990.
Lodge, Sir Oliver, *My Philosophy*,
  Ernest Benn, 1933.
Lomas, Robert, *The Man who Invented the Twentieth Century*,
  Headline, 1999.
Mae-Wan Ho, *The Rainbow and the Worm*,
  World Scientific, 1993.
McTaggart, Lynne, *What Doctors Don't Tell You*,
  Thorsons, 1996.
Murdoch, Iris, *Metaphysics as a Guide to Morals*,
  Penguin, 1993.
Myers, Frederic, *Human Personality and its Survival of Bodily
  Death*, Longmans, Green, and Co., 1907.
Needham, Joseph, *Biochemistry and Morphogenesis*,
  Cambridge University Press, 1942.
  Order and Life, M.I.T. Press, 1968.
Newton, Sir Isaac, *Opticks*,
  Dover Publications, 1979.
Nordenström, Björn E W, *Biologically Closed Electric Circuits*,
  Nordic Medical Publications, 1983.
Nunez, P L, *Electric Fields of the Brain*,
  Oxford University Press, 1981.
O'Neill, John J, *Prodigal Genius. The Life of Nikola Tesla*,

Neville Spearman, 1968.

Oppenheim, Janet, *Physics and psychic research in Victorian and Edwardian England*, Physics Today, May 1986.

Ouspensky, P D, *A New Model of the Universe*, Routledge & Kegan Paul, 1931.

Packard, Alpheus S, *Lamarck, The Founder of Evolution*, Longmans, Green & Co., 1901.

Penfield, Wilder,
The Cerebral Cortex of Man, Macmillan, 1957;
The Mystery of Mind, Princeton University Press, 1975.

Polanyi, Michael, *The Tacit Dimension*, Routledge & Kegan Paul, 1967.

Popper, Karl R, *Objective Knowledge. An Evolutionary Approach*, Oxford University Press, 1972.

Progogine, Ilya, *Self-organisation in Non-equilibrium Systems*, John Wiley & Sons, 1977.

Rose, Lewontin, and Kamin, *Not in our Genes*, Penguin, 1984.

Sheppard, Asher R and Eisenbud, Merril,
Biological Effects of Electric and Magnetic Fields of Extremely Low Frequency, New York University Press, 1977.

Sherrington, Sir Charles, *Man on his Nature*, Cambridge University Press, 1951.

Sherwood, Jane, *The Psychic Bridge*, Psychic Book Club, 1942.

Sinnett, A P, *Esoteric Buddhism*, Theosophical Publishing House, 1883.

Spemann, Hans, *Embryonic Development and Induction*, Yale University Press, 1938.

Steiner, Rudolf,
The Fifth Gospel, Rudolf Steiner Press, 1970;
Man: Hieroglyph of the Universe, Rudolf Steiner Press, 1972.

Sugrue, Thomas, *There is a River*, A.R.E. Press, Virginia, 1973.

Tart, Charles, *Altered States of Consciousness*, John Wiley & Sons, 1969.

Tenforde, T S, (editor), *Magnetic Field Effects on Biological*

Systems, Plenum Press, 1979.
Tesla, Nikola,
    (Lectures, patents, articles), Nikola Tesla Museum, 1956.
    (Colorado Springs Notes 1899-1900), Nolit, 1978.
Thompson, D'Arcy, *On Growth and Form*,
    Cambridge University Press, 1917.
Turing, A M, *The Chemical Basis of Morphogenesis*,
    Philosophical Transactions of the Royal Society, 1952.
Wallace, Alfred Russell, *My Life*,
    Chapman & Hall, 1908.
Walter, W Grey, *The Living Brain*,
    Duckworth, 1953.

Index

Radiation field 34
Rayleigh, Lord 124-
Regeneration 5,23
Reich, Wilhelm 105
Relativity, Theory of 1,127,151
Rhine, J B 101

Schumann waves 51,120
Semitone 32
Shaw, George Bernard 84,90,161
Sheldrake, Rupert 118
Sherrington, Sir Charles 113
Sherwood, Jane 146
Sinnett, A P 133
Skin resistance 6
Smith, Adam 82
Social Darwinism 82-
Sodium ion 3,21
Soliton 8
Somite 30
Spemann, H 36
Spinal nerves 7,21,30
Spinoza 90
Spiritualism 99,124-
SPR 126-
SQUID magnetometer 30,124
Stationary waves 7,24,52
Steiner, Rudolf 120,128,135
String theory 2,55,144
Subtle body 22
Swedenborg 135,144
Synapse 31

Temporal cortex 111
TENS instrument 79
Tesla, Nikola 1,7,40-,78
Tesla-Westinghouse 48
Theosophy 90

Thompson, D'Arcy 19,107
Thomson, J J 58,124-
TMS unstrument 79
Transplantation 69-
Tuned circuit 22,48
Turing, Alan 9,24,33

Wallace. Alfred Russell 131
Wavelength 32
Wertheimer, Nancy 4
Westinghouse, George 41,47
World Telegraphy 52

X-rays 53-

Young, J Z 111